ATLANTA ARCHITECTURE

The Victorian Heritage: 1837-1918

A New Edition of the 1976 Catalog by
Elizabeth A. Lyon
Prepared for an Exhibit at
The Atlanta Historical Society

Book Design: Roy P. Frangiamore

Typography: Merck Typesetting, Inc.

Printing: Phoenix Communications, Inc.

Cover: Terra-Cotta artifact from the old Whitehead Building.

CONTENTS

PREFACE TO THE FIRST EDITION

Concern for Atlanta's architectural history and for its preservation has a long history of its own at the Atlanta Historical Society. During its fifty-year existence, the Society has amassed a large and fine picture collection illustrating Atlanta buildings, as well as a growing file of blueprints and other records from local architectural offices.

The Society's preservation of two important examples of local architecture demonstrates this concern even more dramatically. Members rescued the Tullie Smith House from demolition in 1969. They moved it to the grounds of the Society, restored this farmhouse of the 1840s, and opened it as a house museum. It is a rare local example of the plantation plain-style architecture of piedmont Georgia surviving from the early years of settlement in this region.

Since 1967, the Atlanta Historical Society has centered its activities on the grounds of a spectacular architectural achievement of 1928: The Swan House. Its stylistic precedents lie in eighteenth-century English and earlier Italian country houses. Designed by Philip Shutze, it is Atlanta's supreme expression of the taste for elegant classicism that has continued through the twentieth century to have a strong influence on Atlanta's architecture. Contrasts between the two examples of local architecture preserved by the Society bear witness to Atlanta's remarkable prosperity during the fewer than ninety years that separate the building dates of the two.

The present exhibition focuses attention on "the houses in between"—the architecture that left behind the relative crudities of the plantation plain style—the architecture that preceded the refinements of the classicism which gained dominance of local taste early in this century. Most of the structures featured here cannot command reverence as the very first built by local pioneers. Nor do they inspire emulation as do the fashionable local examples of classical grandeur. Rather they represent an exciting period—the period that gave real form to this city—a period marked by experimentation in a variety of styles.

We have already sacrificed much of the rich architectural heritage left us by Victorian Atlantans. The exuberant structures they built after the Civil War were tangible expressions of the spirit of a "New South," of policies still shaping this city. Ironically, that ambitious, progressive spirit, so fundamental to Atlanta's success, is the same that continues to destroy the irreplaceable landmarks built by the generation that first articulated it.

That spirit needs tempering with understanding that progress in city building should be cumulative, not destructive of everything old. To preserve old buildings, we need not embalm them rendering them lifeless and dependent on continuing charity. They can be adapted to profitable contemporary uses while they lend visual variety, quality, local identity, and human scale to the new urban scene. These attributes of great cities are the essence of their quality of civilization—the key to their long-term success in attracting and holding people.

Old buildings also give the city genuine qualities of historical dimension and color. As John Dos Passos has observed, whether people are entirely conscious of it or not, old buildings add memory and dignity to our daily lives. Rather than concocting nostalgic pseudo-historical structures, our generation needs to recognize genuine and intriguing vestiges of Atlanta's nineteenth-century origins.

The need is not just to turn a few key monuments into museums, but also to save modest buildings which are touchstones to the lives lived by earlier citizens. We still have such structures to save in Underground and in scattered residential neighborhoods. With their numbers diminishing almost daily each takes on added individual importance.

Mounting this exhibition has taught us a great deal about the city's nineteenth-century architectural form. It has also brought into sharper focus political and economic issues arising from attempts to preserve local landmarks. The show confronts the visitor with a long wall of photographs of Atlanta buildings. Wherever appropriate, the photographs have been labeled "Demolished." Affixing those labels was a sobering experience. We became poignantly aware that Atlanta's achitecture once epitomized the excitement and variety of the Victorian era. Most of that has been systematically destroyed. The city is right now, on the verge of losing many of the precious few survivals of its Victorian architectural heritage. They too will go unless many citizens and institutions rally to support the cause of preservation. The Atlanta Historical Society supports that cause and offers this exhibition and catalogue in its service.

Catherine L. Frangiamore
Curator, Atlanta Historical Society

4

PREFACE TO THE SECOND EDITION

Ten years have passed since the Atlanta Historical Society set out to help Atlantans recognize their Victorian heritage through an exhibit on Atlanta architecture. The multimedia exhibit featured photographs of the city's nineteenth and early twentieth century buildings labeled to note those which had been demolished, architectural artifacts gathered from private collections and wrecking yards, and an audiovisual show that ended with a look into the future with the imagined vaporization of the Regency-Hyatt Hotel as an example of an historic building that was no longer valued in the twenty-first century. Since 1976, as a casual glance through this exhibit catalog will show, several more buildings have disappeared, and for most of the period up to 1986 there has been little sustained public attention to the losses or to preservation issues generally.

The Fox Theater, a building whose future was uncertain at the time of the exhibit, has been preserved and, in fact, is now taken for granted by the many who enjoy concerts there; historic preservation has been a major component of the revitalization of many Atlanta neighborhoods; the friends of Piedmont Park have worked with the City toward its renovation; and without much public fanfare several historic downtown buildings have been rehabilitated using investment tax credits for historic preservation. A national conference on Historic Preservation and the Minority Community was held in Atlanta earlier in the decade and several preservation agencies and organizations have been active. The Atlanta Urban Design Commission, a city agency, has worked throughout the decade with the State Historic Preservation Office in the Department of Natural Resources to survey and evaluate what remains of the city's historic buildings and districts, and to recognize their significance through 82 listings on the National Register of Historic Places. The Atlanta Preservation Center, founded in 1980, has educated visitors and citizens alike to Atlanta's remaining heritage through tours of historic districts and publications for children. The Atlanta Historical Society has continued to promote an understanding of the relationship between the city's dynamic history and development and its built environment through exhibits, publications, and lectures. The Georgia Trust for Historic Preservation's fund-raising activities have brought hundreds of Atlanta citizens into buildings and areas such as the Fairlie-Poplar district, The Biltmore Hotel, Rhodes Hall, and Baltimore Place to enjoy and appreciate the city's unique historic spaces.

Perhaps it is the steady growth in preservation activity over the decade by public agencies and private organizations that has raised public awareness. Perhaps it is the concern raised by such crises as the threat to the nationally significant Olmsted Parks and Parkways of Druid Hills, the demolition of historic buildings along Atlanta's famed Peachtree Street, and the realization that little remains along that famous road or in downtown Atlanta to remind us of our past. Perhaps it is simply a growth in a general preservation and conservation ethic nurtured by programs like the National Register of Historic Places and the various preservation opportunities it encourages. Probably it is a combination of all these events and activities, but whatever is responsible there is no doubt that in 1986 historic preservation has suddenly engaged the attention of Atlanta's media and citizens.

Why has it taken Atlantans so long to realize that so much of what provides richness, variety, and continuity in their built environment is gone? Undoubtedly it is the irony of the philosophy of "new is better" that has made the city grow and prosper: The Atlantans of the Victorian era, just as Atlantans today, believed that new development was progress. Today, as then, there is a general belief that what is "new" and "bigger" is of necessity "better." "Tear it down, build it bigger and better," Dudley Glass wrote in the *City Builder*, a forerunner of *Atlanta* Magazine in 1929. This statement of almost sixty years ago sounds curiously contemporary to Atlantans today watching the demolition of historic buildings for the construction of the latest in ever taller and newer structures and listening to the justification for this construction as the new "historic character of Atlanta."

A look at some of these structures or at the parking lots which have replaced buildings illustrated in this catalog should prove instructive. New buildings that look historic and glass-walled towers cannot substitute for the distinct character, visual interest, and sense of place provided by real historic buildings in their original settings. Even so, contemporary structures that respect the scale and character of older buildings can provide a sense of continuity with earlier periods when Atlantans created the prosperity that we enjoy today. The debate, born of crisis and conflict but now being channeled into an informed preservation planning process, can lead to the preservation and wise use of what now remains of the heritage chronicled in this catalog. The preservation of our remaining significant historic buildings can provide economic and social benefits to the future.

Reprinting of *Atlanta Architecture: The Victorian Heritage* has been made possible through the generosity of Frank "Duke" Steinemann. The pieces of our past exhibited in the One Georgia Center remind us of the rich and varied craftsmanship of our past and encourage us to value such work where we can find it. The reprinting of this catalog of an exhibit designed to help Atlantans appreciate their heritage is an important statement of interest and concern by Steinemann and Company. The generosity of Duke Steinemann will be appreciated by all who believe that the continuity of history is important to the quality of Atlanta's future.

—Elizabeth A. Lyon

October 1986

ACKNOWLEDGMENTS

The exhibition "Atlanta Architecture: The Victorian Heritage" and this catalogue have been made possible by a grant from the National Endowment for the Humanities. The trustees, staff, and members of the Atlanta Historical Society gratefully acknowledge the Endowment's generous support of our efforts to use the rich collections of this Society in interpretive exhibitions. We are also grateful for additional financial support for the project which came from the Bureau of Cultural and International Affairs of the City of Atlanta.

Dr. Elizabeth M. Lyon's research was the basis for this entire project. Her concentrated study of Atlanta's architecture began as work on a master's thesis at Emory University, continued through presentation of her Emory dissertation in 1971, "Business Buildings in Atlanta: A Study in Urban Growth and Form," and has expanded into survey and preservation planning work for the city of Atlanta and for the state.

Basic concepts for the exhibition grew from a cooperative effort of the project principals. Roy P. Frangiamore's conception and design of the installation made visible much of the richness of the architecture and focused attention on important aspects of the preservation cause. Project Administrator Bettijo H. Cook uncovered and assembled an unanticipated wealth of fragments from lost buildings. Project Director Catherine Lynn Frangiamore wrote text for exhibition panels, helped with installation, and edited this manuscript. Patricia M. Reed assisted tirelessly through every phase of installation of the show and preparation of the catalogue. Richard T. Eltzroth aided in retrieval of photographs from the Society's archive. Vernon Paine's help with installation is greatly appreciated, as is the work of Donna Berry, Mark Clemons, Craig Mendelson, and Betsy Threefoot.

For their typing we thank Sharon Jaudon, Lillian Salter, and Peggy Haverty, as well as Elma Kurtz, who also contributed vital editorial work. Grace Sherry gave valuable assistance in preparing the final manuscript for the printer. We thank Franklin Garrett, Historian of the City of Atlanta, for identifying and locating many structures. We thank Margot Gayle, President of the Friends of Cast Iron Architecture, for identifying sources of some cast iron store fronts in antebellum Atlanta. We are grateful to the many friends of the Society who assisted in the installation of the exhibition, including Jim Fuller, Julia Jones, Randy Jones, Marianna Lines, Liz Malone, Anne Salter, Frank Walsh, and Ernest and Gerry Williams. We also thank designer Robert Griggs for aid in locating architectural fragments, Timothy Crimmins of Georgia State University and Gloria Blackwell of Atlanta University for their critical review of the catalogue text. Finally we thank our docents for their volunteer help with this exhibition: Olive Barnett, Flora Bynum, Joan Cowles, Helen Crawford, Edith Huguley, Ann Montgomery, Mary Patton, Peggy Poer, Ann Potter, Maggie Rankin, Dolly Tillander, Grace Trimble, Bette Smith, Sylvia Worthington, and Mary Wright.

Much of what we have been able to show in this exhibition and include in the catalogue is only suggestive, and the relatively brief period in which it has been developed has led unavoidably to errors and omissions. However, we look upon the experience and the results as parts of an ongoing process. More basic work is needed. Local residential architecture and the work influenced by the Arts and Crafts Movement are still to be studied in depth. We look forward to a rounding out of the study of Atlanta's architecture.

Acknowledgements for the second edition of 1986 include, from the Georgia Department of Natural Resources, Historic Preservation Section, Elizabeth A. Lyon for a new preface and updated material, Kenneth H. Thomas, Jr., for architectural research, and James R. Lockhart for photographic research. The staff of the Atlanta Historical Society providing assistance included John H. Ott, executive director; Jane Powers Weldon, director of publications; and Elaine Kirkland and William F. Hull of the archives staff.

LENDERS TO THE EXHIBITION

The Atlanta Historical Society gratefully acknowledges the cooperation and generosity of the following

Atlanta Public Library

Mr. L. M. Becknell

Cathedral of St. Philip

Mrs. William Conard

Continental Wrecking Corporation

Mr. and Mrs. Edward Daugherty

Miss Nancy Downing

Emory University, Department of the History of Art

Emory University, Special Collections

Mr. Jim Fuller

Georgia Institute of Technology, Architectural Library

Mr. Robert Griggs

Mr. Harold Hudgins, Hudgins & Co., Inc.

Mrs. Robert Jones III

Mr. and Mrs. William Mann

Mr. and Mrs. John Merritt

Mrs. Elizabeth MacGregor

Mrs. Bruce Montgomery

Mr. and Mrs. H. English Robinson

Mrs. M. T. Salter, Jr.

Mr. and Mrs. Bealy Smith

Southern Technical Institute

Mr. and Mrs. Andrew Sparks

1837 Victoria ascends the throne of England.

1837 A survey team headed by Stephen H. Long places a stake in the ground of present-day central Atlanta to mark the terminus point for the building of the state-owned Western and Atlantic Railroad line south from Chattanooga. The southern terminus of the line, established later a few hundred yards east of the original point is now marked by the Zero Mile Post still visible under the Central Avenue viaduct.

1843 The pioneer settlement of Terminus is incorporated as Marthasville.

1847 The small village becomes the City of Atlanta with a population of about 500 persons and a charter designating its area as a circle whose radius measures one mile out from the Zero Mile Post.

1850 **POPULATION 2,572**

1852 John Boutell, the only pre-Civil War architect of record, arrives in the city from New England.

1853 The first Atlanta Passenger Depot, an early United States example of the iron-arched train shed, is constructed in the center of the city.

1854 Atlanta City Hall-Fulton County Courthouse is built to serve government needs of the young city and a newly created county.

1858 Atlanta's first iron store front arrives from Daniel Badger's New York City iron works and is placed in Beach and Root's dry goods store on Whitehall Street.

1860 **POPULATION 9,554**

1860 Abraham Lincoln is elected to the Presidency of the United States.

1861 Civil War breaks out.

1864 The Battle of Atlanta, now memorialized in the Cyclorama in Grant Park, brings about the occupation of the city by Union troops.

1864 A large area of the city is destroyed on November 14 by departing Union troops.

1868 William H. Parkins becomes the first professional to open an office for the practice of architecture after the Civil War.

1869 The first building of the new Atlanta University, North Hall, is constructed on "Diamond Hill" overlooking the city.

1869 State government moves from Milledgeville to Atlanta, after designation of the city as the capital in 1868. Government officials move into the refurbished and completed building at the corner of Marietta and Forsyth streets which had begun as Kimball's Opera House.

1870 **POPULATION 31,789**

1870 The first passenger elevators in Atlanta are built into the new Kimball House Hotel.

1870-
1871 The Union Depot II is constructed on the site of the destroyed antebellum structure.

1871 Atlanta's first street railroad with horse-and-mule drawn cars begins operation.

1873 A wrought iron bridge replaces an older wood and iron structure which carries Broad Street over the railroad and provides the only safe passage over the tracks in the center of the city.

1876 America's Centennial Exposition in Philadelphia displays the technological achievements and architectural forms of the age.

1879 A telephone is installed in the Kimball House.

1879 Alexander C. Bruce opens an office with William Parkins

and hires the first architectural draftsman in the city.

1879 Four architect's firms are now in practice.

1880 **POPULATION 37,409**

1881 International Cotton Exposition in Atlanta exhibits cotton manufactures and raw material.

1881 First structural iron columns manufactured in Atlanta for the Moore-Marsh Building.

1881-
1883 Fulton County Courthouse built.

1884-
1889 The present Georgia State Capitol Building, now a National Historic Landmark, is constructed.

1885 Mayor Hillyer proposes that bridges coordinated with a new railroad depot be built in the center of the city.

1889 The Georgia Institute of Technology is opened in High Victorian buildings of the upcoming architectural firm of Bruce and Morgan.

1889 *The Southern Architect and Building News* is founded and begins publishing in Atlanta.

1889 Electricity replaces gas in the city's street lamps. The first Atlanta "electric" street railway, an early United States example, begins running between the suburb of Inman Park and downtown.

1890 **POPULATION 65,533**

1890 Early residences are built in Inman Park, Atlanta's first planned, residential suburb.

1891 The names of ten architects' firms appear in The City Directory.

1892 The South's pioneer skyscraper, the Equitable Building, opens its doors for business.

1893 The World's Columbian Exposition in Chicago sets precedents for classical architecture and monumental planning.

1895 The Cotton States and International Exposition in Piedmont Park advertises Atlanta as a regional transportation center.

1897 The building of the narrow, triangular skyscraper, the English-American Building, pre-dates the "Flatiron" or Fuller Building, in New York City.

1900 Seventeen architectural firms are in practice at the turn of the century.

1906 A charter is granted to the Atlanta Chapter of the American Institute of Architects.

1908 A four-year professional course in architecture is opened to students at the Georgia Institute of Technology.

1909 Atlanta architect Haralson Bleckley presents his Plaza Plan for covering the railroad gulch in central Atlanta with a platform of walkways and landscaped areas. This plan was never implemented.

1916 A Registration Law, written by Thomas H. Morgan, providing for the registration and licensing of architects, is approved by the Atlanta Chapter, American Institute of Architects. It will be passed by the Georgia Legislature in 1919.

1917 America enters World War I. A new community flag pole, designed by architect W. T. Downing, is placed at Five Points in the center of the business district.

1918 Thirty-four architectural firms are listed in The City Directory.

1918 The building of Brookwood Station, a suburban passenger depot to serve the expanding northside residential areas signals the growth of suburban areas.

INTRODUCTION

Atlanta presents a dynamic and progressive image to the world in this Bicentennial year. But, in that image there is not much evidence of her origins and development. If there are references to the past, they are often cast in the context of a persistent myth: That myth supposes that Atlanta was a gracious, Old South town that was destroyed in the fires of the Civil War. If there is acknowledgment of a New South, it is the contemporary New South of modern buildings and sprawling suburbs. Seldom is the New South of the nineteenth century mentioned, almost as if it had been obliterated from memory as its buildings have been demolished.

Yet, the origins of Atlanta as a railroad terminus and the developments that produced the present vigorous urban environment belong to that almost forgotten period. Atlanta's heritage is Victorian. The stake that was to mark the terminus point of the Western and Atlantic Railroad line south from Chattanooga was driven into the ground of present day central Atlanta in 1837. In that same year Queen Victoria ascended the throne of England. The period which bears her name was well underway by the time a frontier settlement called Atlanta grew up around that terminus point. Atlanta's subsequent rapid development from railroad terminus to regional center depended upon the expanding technology and aggressive economic attitudes of the Victorian age. The city's physical appearance was cast in the architectural forms of the period.

New scholarship is helping us to understand the Victorian age. Such knowledge is essential to our understanding of Atlanta. The Victorian building art in Atlanta, as in other areas of the country, was a bold and often imaginative response to the achievements made possible by new technologies and the problems created by rapid urban growth.

Yet, Americans have been unsympathetic to the Victorian past and have made little attempt to understand the buildings and culture of an era out of fashion. Fashions in architecture change much as do styles in clothing and automobiles. Buildings, though made of relatively permanent materials, can nevertheless be up-dated in conformity with the prevailing styles. As Atlantans prospered after the Civil War, many of them adorned early and often unpretentious houses with architectural features of the new Victorian styles. For example, the William Loundes Calhoun residence, built soon after the Civil War, started life as a cottage. The Calhouns enlarged it in the 1870s adding a second story (below) and a double-deck porch with fancy wooden cut work in the balustrades. Again in the eighties the family up-dated their home, burying its original symmetry under turrets, gables, and elaborate wooden ornaments.

Even houses which were originally more stylish, like the antebellum Leyden residence, received up-to-date treatment during the Reconstruction period. A Second Empire mansard roof, which later burned, was added to this Italianate mansion sometime before 1880 (below). Even if this Victorian addition to a classically detailed house had not burned, it is possible it would have been removed at the turn of the century as building tastes changed once again.

In the Late Victorian era, which lasted in spirit down to World War I, American taste again changed. Beaux-arts classicism and a taste for academically correct and pure architectural forms became dominant. The lingering influence of such tastes has been one of the barriers to the appreciation of nineteenth century Victorian architecture.

Architects of our own era, whether trained in schools dominated by Beaux-arts ideas or by modern architectural theories, have not placed much value on Victorian buildings. Some scholars, too, have added confusion to the existing distaste by considering architecture in the nineteenth century to be a "battle of styles." Observing a parade of overlapping styles and modes, they have concluded that it was an architecture lacking any basic unity or clearly recognizable form. Layman, architects, and scholars alike need to take a new and fresh look at the buildings of the nineteenth century.

The present exhibition seeks to introduce the rich architectural heritage of nineteenth century Atlanta to a public that has tended to look for its past in the Greek Revival mansions of the early nineteenth century rural South. With this exhibition we hope to encourage an appreciation of Victorian architecture and an understanding that it was based on serious aesthetic theories.

Calhoun Residence

Leyden Residence

We introduce the distinction between finely designed buildings and the gaudy fantasies which are the only structures which many are accustomed to calling Victorian. From this we hope to encourage an understanding of nineteenth century architecture as an expression of an intensely interesting and exciting period in American history, a period which had particular significance for the city of Atlanta.

Through articles and scholarly studies of recent years, the architecture of the Victorian period is gaining recognition as a serious body of work based on consistent and coherent design principles. In a period of exploding new ideas and startling inventions, Victorian architects took a new approach to the building art. Believing themselves to be the beneficiaries of all the cultures of all the ages, they searched the entire body of historical architecture for style elements which could be used to create a new architecture. Such an approach was the basis of Victorian eclecticism. The goal was not to recreate a particular historical style, but to use elements of many styles as resource material for the creation of a new architecture.

As a prototype for such creative eclecticism, an architect who had come from Alabama to Atlanta in 1881, John H. Moser, proposed a building for the American Institute of Architects where "every epoch in architectural history shall be represented by details from the best examples now obtainable, following each other in orderly sequence." Moser hoped that by incorporating and synthesizing the qualities and details from many styles into building designs, a new and distinctly American style could be created (Page 90). Moser and his contemporaries looked to the great buildings of the past for historical inspiration and detail. Some American architects traveled abroad to seek out the great buildings of the past, but few Atlanta architects had the opportunity to travel widely. Gottfried L. Norrman, who had emigrated to America from Sweden, arriving in Atlanta in the 1880s, had perhaps seen the buildings of Europe. Alfred Eichberg, another Atlanta figure of the 1880s, had completed his technical education in Heidelberg, Germany. But the majority of the architects who came in increasing numbers into the growing southern city of the 1880s and 1890s learned their profession as apprentices.

In the nineteenth century, Atlanta architects worked in offices, which according to local architect Thomas Henry Morgan, were not only workshops where "the practical business of the day was always uppermost, but where each took on the character of the studio." The personnel of the office always included a little group of architectural students, Morgan reported, who were encouraged by the office principals to study the accepted examples and the history of architecture. The course of study, Morgan remembered, centered on "the five orders of architecture according to Vignola, the historic styles, Ferguson's *History of Architecture*, Rickman's *Gothic Architecture*, and other standard works."

While architectural history was the source of a new architectural language, and while pattern books and journals added design ideas and information to the architect's vocabulary, nature provided principles of composition and organization. Calvert Vaux, one of the nineteenth century's most influential architects, wrote: "The great charm in the forms of natural landscape, lies in its well-balanced irregularity." For the classical ideals of formal balance and proportion, admired by their Greek Revival predecessors, Victorian designers substituted the "picturesque." Influenced at mid-century by Andrew Jackson Downing, who maintained that buildings of strong character and forceful expression depended upon irregularity and a partial want of proportion and symmetry, architects developed a picturesque method of design. Freely composing masses, building elements,

and interior spaces, they created plans and buildings of great variety.

Building masses, especially in residential structures, projected into the landscape. No longer did designers force the shapes of rooms to fit into the confines of square or rectangular boxes that would present smooth, symmetrical facades. Rather, in planning the shapes and arrangements of rooms, they gave precedence to consideration of their use, convenience, and exposure.

The old-fashioned central axial approach to an entrance, that previously would have been a formal portico, was replaced by a pathway to an entrance tucked away under a rambling veranda. Windows were grouped in a variety of combinations: On a facade they were sometimes grouped in twos and threes under arches. In other instances, several single windows were placed on a facade under headings of various shapes. Roof lines blossomed with an array of chimneys, gables, cupolas, and parapets. Walls were enriched with pattern, texture, and color.

Most arbiters of taste felt that white paint on walls presented too great a contrast to natural foliage. It was given up in favor of darker and more subdued colors. An infinite variety of color and surface texture was created by the use not only of applied color, but also of contrasting materials like brick and terra cotta, rough and smooth stone, and by the juxtaposition of masonry and wood trim.

Variety itself was valued. This attitude was voiced in the public response to one of Victorian Atlanta's most important buildings, the Kimball House (Page 34). Commenting on the opening of this splendid structure, the local newspaper pointed out that " . . . the facade is very much broken, and the observer never fails to see some new point of interest from whatever view he may behold it, and yet every part is in perfect harmony with every other part. . . ."

The same newspaper reported a few years later, in 1893, that Atlanta's streets were lined with "diversified styles of picturesque architecture. Palatial residences, pretty cottages, and stately business blocks and public buildings showed an infinite variety of form and color and material taste." Such buildings were given style names like "Queen Anne," "French Empire," "Romanesque Revival," and, simply, "Cottage." These style names were only suggestive. Variety was the goal pursued within each design to create individual combinations for particular buildings. Local observers thus recognized, if they did not fully explain, the two major components of Victorian architecture: the picturesque, and eclecticism. Picturesque-eclecticism, a designation which incorporates both creative eclecticism and the picturesque design method, has become almost a style name for this architecture.

While ideas about picturesque composition and design diversity informed their work, nineteenth century architects also developed ideas about the appropriateness of certain styles to particular kinds of buildings. The Greek and Roman styles had been used in America for government buildings since Thomas Jefferson's day because of their associations with democracy and republicanism. Religious aspirations and scholarly ideals associated with the Middle Ages dictated the use of Gothic Revival styles for many churches as well as the use both of Gothic elements and massive Romanesque forms for college buildings. Such associative symbolism continues to influence these building types today.

Historical styles with particular symbolic references could be used appropriately for established building types like government buildings and churches, but new building types spawned by previously unknown technologies lacked precedent in the historical record. These demanded new forms. Atlanta's railroad buildings fall into this second category. The city's first railroad station was simply an iron-arched roof on walls of brick arches (Page 12). Its post Civil War replacement was a larger iron-arched enclosure in a uniquely Victorian form (Page 23); picturesque walls and towers were fronted by a great iron fan which expressed the shed behind. This structure was overshadowed in 1905 by Terminal Station (Page 64), a building which gave up the expression of the iron shed in favor of creating a symbolic gateway to the city. This was in keeping with the contemporary revival of interest in classical monumental styles stimulated by the buildings of the World's Columbian Exposition at Chicago in 1893 and by architects who had studied abroad.

The skyscraper, one of the proudest achievements of the nineteenth century, also grew from new technological and economic forces. Iron construction, elevators, and new mechanical systems, increasing population density, rising land costs, and a growing office profession came together in Chicago in 1884 to produce the first steel skeleton office building. In Atlanta, iron columns had appeared along business streets in the 1850s (Page 14), and elevators were included in the first Kimball House in 1870. Steel-framed office buildings were built here in the 1890s.

Atlanta's earliest tall buildings were designed by Chicago and New York architects who had been part of the early skyscraper development. The first tall buildings by Atlanta architects reflected their knowledge of the pioneer modern buildings of the Chicago School. Like their colleagues in other cities, they tried various approaches to the design of tall buildings. The most common was a three-part composition of base, shaft, and capital, found in the English-American Building (Page 57) and the Empire Building (Page 67).

Architectural practice, too, felt the impact of technological change. Blueprints, now taken for granted by builders, were unknown in Atlanta before 1880. Only one set of heavy brown paper drawings and handwritten specifications, bound and backed with cloth, was available for each building operation. Few of these ink and crayon or watercolor drawings came through the building operation intact. Therefore, few of the early drawings survive. We can sympathize with architect Morgan when he described the plans and specifications of his first Atlanta employer, William H. Parkins: "Mr. Parkins wrote a beautiful Spencerian style and in the margins he drew pen and ink freehand sketches that clearly illustrated his meaning. When finished [it] was a real work of art and it seemed a pity to turn it over to the builder."

According to Mr. Morgan, it was in about 1881 that, following instructions for a recently developed method of making blueprint copies from original drawings on tracing cloth which he found in the *Scientific American*, the first blueprint copy of an Atlanta drawing was made in the office of Bruce and Morgan. Soon thereafter, Morgan recalled, the typewriter became a standard item of office equipment and duplicates of building specifications accompanied blueprint copies of the drawings to the construction site.

Architect Morgan's description of nineteenth century building practice not only records the details of architectural practice but provides as well significant insight into nineteenth century craftsmanship and Atlanta building trades. With obvious fondness, Morgan described the carpenters who studied publications on carpentry and joinery and arrived at the building site with large tool chests filled with every sort of hand woodworking tool; the sheet metal workers who were "artists" in fashioning the galvanized iron work for cornices, window caps, columns, and pilaster capitals; and the plumbers and other mechanics who experimented and solved construction problems on the job. Morgan wrote that many contractors not only did the building but also manufactured and carried in stock a large part of the material required for construction. Planing mills and brick yards were operated by these men.

In 1871, Pellegrino Pellegrini established a company to manufacture artificial stone and soon opened with Zack Castleberry the first terra cotta works in the South. Pellegrini and Castleberry later became the Southern Terra-Cotta Works and continued making terra cotta for Atlanta buildings until 1912 (Page 99.)

Iron columns had appeared in building facades before the Civil War, and bridge beams and columns were available from an Atlanta company by the late seventies. However, it was not until much later that the first structural iron building columns were manufactured in Atlanta. They were made by the Atlanta Machine Works for the Moore-Marsh Building in 1881 (Page 36).

In addition to effecting changes in building types and architectural methods, the new technologies and inventions of the Victorian age influenced the growth of densely occupied urban centers, produced unsettling changes in the urban environment, and created enormous municipal problems. Such conditions were bound to affect both the practice and the form of architecture. If Atlanta was neither as large nor as densely settled as her older northern counterparts, she nevertheless faced similar problems created by rapid changes and growth. Her architects and builders responded in similar ways.

Atlanta's characteristic nineteenth century buildings not only represent the styles and aesthetic ideas of a unique period but also provide a cultural record. We can "read" these buildings on site where standing, in many photographs which fortunately survive even when the buildings do not, and in the written record. The buildings are documents of the city's history. Attitudes about style and form reflecting social and economic history, as well as technological change and commercial development, were expressed in them.

Much of this record reflects general American developments, for example, the movement from rural areas into urban centers, industrialization and the mass production of goods and services, technological change in building trades, and in urban transportation the blurring of regional distinctions, and the generally growing complexity of life. Yet, the buildings and the urban pattern which they produced are also images of a specific city which was built up at a particular time.

"Atlanta's Architecture: The Victorian Heritage" is a multimedia exhibition that has been designed to display the visual richness and historical interest in the city's buildings. What follows is both a summary of the highlights of that exhibition and of the Victorian architectural heritage which it represents. Buildings and artifacts have been chosen to represent a range of building forms, the work of notable architects, patterns of life and work, and the key historical buildings.

ATLANTA IN 1864

FULTON COUNTY JAIL • CITY HALL SOLOMON RES. • CREW RES. TRINITY CHURCH • NEAL RES. •
GA R R ENGINE HOUSE 2 ST PHILIPS CH • CENTL PRESB CH • 2d BAPTIST CH •
MOUND HOUSE WASHINGTON HALL CITY PARK • IMMACULATE CONCEPTION CH • AMERICAN HOTEL •
LOYD ST • M & W FREIGHT DEPOT • CITY MARKET • CALABOOSE ENGINE HOUSE 1
MASONIC HALL TROUT HOUSE • CAR SHED • ATLANTA HOTEL • GA R R BANK CONCERT HALL INTELLIGENCER OFFICE JACK'S BAKERY C·S·A BRIDGE
PRYOR ST • ATHENÆUM FIVE POINTS NORCROSS' STORE GEN MARCUS WRIGHTS HDQRS WADLEY (FORSYTH) ST • MARIETTA ST
PEACHTREE ST • BRIDGE (BROAD) ST • WALTON ST • TALLULAH FIRE CO ST LUKES CH

Birdseye View of Atlanta in 1864. Painting, Wilbur C. Kurtz, C. 1950. Original in collection of Beverly M. DuBose.

After careful research, Mr. Kurtz was able to delineate the pre-Civil War appearance of the growing city. The view reveals a town centered around railroad tracks and railroad buildings. With the exception of a few landmarks like the City Hall-County Courthouse and several churches, the scene was dominated by commercial buildings and residences of little architectural pretension.

Atlanta's antebellum buildings were products of the Early Victorian period when the influence of the classical styles which had created the Greek Revival architecture commonly associated with the Old South was waning. In public buildings like the City Hall-County Courthouse, the formality of such styles was continued because of their association with Greek democracy and the Roman Republic. However, the beginnings of Victorian diversity were everywhere evident.

Italianate was the most common style for business buildings and stylish residences; Gothic Revival elements appeared in simple frame churches; but plain and utilitarian buildings were most abundant. Buildings were generally the products of anonymous builders although occasionally a designer's name appears. One Columbus Hughes is recorded as the designer of the City Hall, while E. A. Vincent, the city's first map maker, drew the plans for the Passenger Depot. John Boutell, a builder, carpenter, and contractor, is the only Atlantan who we know called himself "architect" during this period.

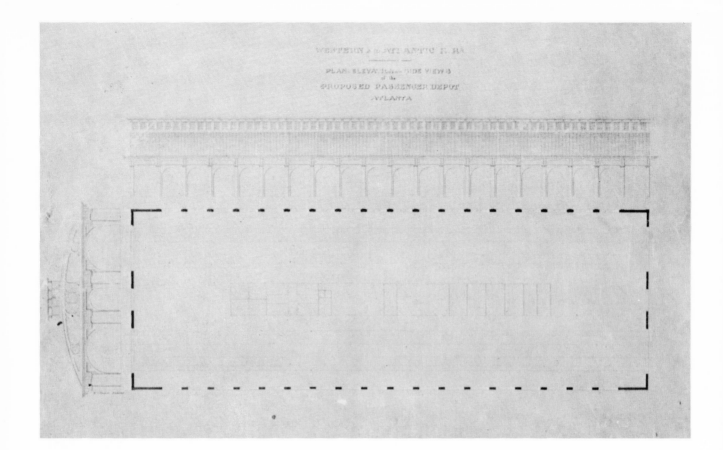

Passenger Depot I, E. A. Vincent, 1853. **Between Pryor and Loyd (renamed Central Avenue) streets. Destroyed 1864. Drawing, Atlanta Historical Society Collections.**

This is the earliest known Atlanta architectural drawing. It shows a simple, iron-arched shed, topped by a skylight running the full length of the building. The arched roof rested on walls of brick arches. At the center of the building, between the tracks, the drawing shows ladies' and gentlemen's "waiting saloons," baggage, and other utilitarian rooms.

Atlanta's first passenger depot was built within one year of the first American iron-arched railroad station in Philadelphia. It was an impressive central feature of the antebellum city. Little is known about its designer, E. A. Vincent, who arrived from England in 1852 and drew the city's first map.

12

Georgia Railroad and Banking Company Building, architect unknown, c. 1855. **Northeast corner Whitehall Street and the Railroad. Destroyed 1864. Photograph of Whitehall at the Georgia Railroad, 1864, Atlanta Historical Society Collections.**

Surrounding the Passenger Depot were the brick and frame utilitarian buildings of the commercial center which grew up around the railroad terminal. When these buildings were self-consciously designed beyond the simplest utilitarian needs, they took the form of Italianate blocks. The Georgia Railroad and Banking Company, one of the most important businesses of the young city, was housed in such a block. The building's hipped roof, dormer window, paired eaves brackets, and doorway framed by classically derived pilasters, entablature and low pediment, were typical features.

American Hotel, architect unknown, 1853. **Southeast corner, Alabama and Pryor streets. Burned 1889. Photograph, 1882, Atlanta Historical Society Collections.**

Known before the war as the Planters' Hotel, this three-story brick hotel was reopened in late 1865 or early 1866 as the American Hotel. Its three stories, brick construction, and crisp white detailing were similar to several antebellum hotel buildings destroyed in the war.

ATLANTA, GEORGIA,

AS IT APPEARED ON THE ENTRANCE OF THE UNION ARMY UNDER GEN. SHERMAN, SEPT. 2ND 1864

View of Decatur and Peach Tree Streets from Marietta Street Looking South

N° 2

Business Buildings 1850s. **General view in 1864. Whitehall and Decatur streets (vicinity present Central City Park). Destroyed 1864. Lithograph, E. B. and E. C. Kellogg, Hartford, Connecticut, from a sketch by D. R. Brown, 1864, Atlanta Historical Society Collections.**

This characteristic streetscape was created by rows of Italianate business buildings. They often incorporated technological innovations: the use of iron columns to support upper facade sections of brick. Cast iron facades were becoming common in New York City and other northern cities in the 1850s and were also found in prewar Atlanta. Beach and Root's 1858 three-story store on Whitehall Street was the earliest Atlanta example. In 1859, Hunnicutt and Taylor, whose shop is shown in this print, announced the opening of their business in the new iron-fronted Collier Building.

Some of the iron fronts were shipped to Atlanta from Daniel Badger's Architectural Iron Works in New York City. Badger was one of the most influential nineteenth century manufacturers of iron building components. Established in 1847, his company was one of several important New York and Philadelphia manufacturers who shipped iron building parts to all sections of the country, and surviving records document shipments of iron store fronts from New York to Atlanta for the Beach and Root Building and the Collier Building.

14

Atlanta City Hall-County Courthouse, Columbus Hughes, 1854. Site of present Georgia State Capitol. Demolished 1884. Lithographs, Atlanta Historical Society Collections.

Only the name of the architect, Columbus Hughes, is recorded in city council proceedings for this dignified government building. It survived the wartime destruction of the city only to be given up when the City of Atlanta offered the site to the state for a capitol building. The structure was reminiscent of early American public buildings in its modest scale and classical detailing. It was a brick cube with stone quoins at the corners, a projecting entrance framed by columns and entablature, and a balustrade running around the edge of the low pyramidal roof. The simply articulated tall octagonal cupola must have asserted a suitably dominant presence in the early city.

ATLANTA, GEORGIA,

Atlanta Medical College, John Boutell, 1854. College Avenue (renamed Coca-Cola Place). Demolished 1906. Photograph of lithograph, Atlanta Historical Society Collections. From E. Y. Clarke's _Illustrated History of Atlanta_, 1879.

Its style displayed associations with New England, perhaps because the architect who designed the Atlanta Medical College had come South from Massachusetts for his health in 1852. Boutell's earliest Atlanta buildings were designed with the restraint of Greek Revival buildings with which he was familiar. His later designs were varied by details and proportions of Italianate derivation. The Medical College with its plain walls, inset entrance framed by simplified classical details, balustrade and wide, low, classically articulated cupola, was one of his earliest Atlanta designs.

CENTRAL PRESBYTERIAN CHURCH, ATLANTA.

Some of the Washington Street churches of antebellum Atlanta also revealed earlier, possibly New England, antecedents. Central Presbyterian Church and Second Baptist Church stood in the same block on Washington Street facing City Hall. Both had tall, multi-staged steeples. A pedimented portico on Corinthian columns led into Central Presbyterian. Double entries flanking a projecting tower base in Second Baptist were framed by columns and pediments. Italianate brackets decorated the tower of this second impressive structure.

16

John Boutell Residence, John Boutell, c. 1852. 138 N. Collins Street (renamed Courtland Street). Demolished 1938. Photograph, Atlanta Historical Society Collections.

Architect John Boutell built his own house on Collins Street at the southwest corner of Ellis Street, not long after his arrival in Atlanta from Massachusetts. It was a wooden, weatherboarded Greek Revival house not unlike many that had been built throughout the northern states during the previous two decades. In the main block, a triangular gable over pilasters and entablature expressed the temple-front motif of larger Greek Revival houses like Bulloch Hall which survives in nearby Roswell. A low wing under an A-line roof at right angles to the house was carefully detailed with horizontal boards. The entrance was correctly framed with modified classical elements.

John Collier Residence, architect unknown, 1858. 45 Nelson Street. Demolished 1930s. Photograph, Atlanta Historical Society Collections.

Perhaps more typical of antebellum Atlanta than the architect-designed buildings were structures like the house built by Judge John Collier. His house shows the changing taste of the 1850s and 1860s with dark masonry walls and dormered mansard roof. In a gesture to the past and perhaps to his position, the Judge attached monumental columns to his asymmetrically placed porch.

17

Grander scale Greek motifs were used by the architect later in the decade for the Leyden House. Here, a peripheral colonnade of slender Ionic columns surrounded the front and sides of the central block. Detailing of exceptionally tall windows and of the entranceway was thinner and less specifically Greek in form than in Boutell's earlier buildings, suggesting the beginning of change.

This house was unusually grand and architecturally ambitious for Atlanta. Although it epitomizes the popular image of the antebellum southern mansion, it was very much the exception in the prewar railroad town.

While some of the antebellum houses on the hills surrounding the city (for example, the William Wilson House in what is now Southwest Atlanta), were columned mansions, the type of house built by Col. L. P. Grant on his vast land holdings in Southeast Atlanta was more up-to-date and characteristic of the period. It was an Italianate block with porches on square posts along the front and side facades, paired eaves brackets and dormers. Grant later donated a portion of his estate to the city for a park, and the remains of his residence are surrounded by later residential buildings.

Sidney Root-Joseph E. Brown Residence, architect unknown, 1858.
**159 Washington Street. Demolished 1927. Photograph, Atlanta
Historical Society Collections.**

According to his memoirs, Atlanta merchant Sidney Root built this
Italianate house out of concrete. Unfortunately, no further documentation
of this claim exists, and it is not possible to determine from the photograph's evidence whether the house was of masonry covered by stucco or
actually of cast concrete. If the latter, it could have been a very early
example, not only in Atlanta but in America. Yet, Sidney Root was a
progressive citizen who was the first Atlantan to put up an iron-fronted
building, the Beach and Root Building of 1858.

*John Neal Residence, John Boutell, 1859, later used as Girls'
High School.* **47 Washington Street, site of present City Hall.
Demolished 1929. Photograph, Atlanta Historical Society Collec-
tions.**

Boutell's designs became more Italianate in later work like this red brick,
two-and-a-half story residence with its Corinthian columns, corner
quoins, eaves brackets, and stained glass cupola.

Built for a planter-merchant from Zebulon, Georgia, who fled the city
during the war, this house became General Sherman's headquarters.
It later was used as a hotel before becoming Girls' High School in
1873.

A few larger city and country houses built in the area that is now the city of Atlanta were monumentally Italianate. But the more typical were simple, so called plantation plain-style buildings such as the Tullie Smith House preserved by the Atlanta Historical Society. The two-story section of the house is one room deep. A low shed roof in the back covers two smaller rooms on the ground floor. One end of the porch, which runs the full length of the house, was enclosed to provide a room for visiting parsons and other travelers.

RECONSTRUCTION

1865-1879

General View, Whitehall Street at Railroad Crossing, 1875. Photograph, Atlanta Historical Society Collections.

Railroad tracks and business buildings continued to create a busy and congested scene in postwar Atlanta. In the background is the cupola of the antebellum steeple of the Central Presbyterian Church and a few surviving prewar business buildings on the south side of Alabama Street. The square steeple topped with pinnacle on the extreme right is the new Church of the Immaculate Conception (Page 29).

he reconstructed city quickly grew up along the old outlines. Buildings were taller by one or two stories, but church spires still dominated the skyline. Architects, drawn to the rapidly growing city, began to work in the new picturesque-eclectic manner. The ready acceptance here of architectural styles like those becoming popular in the North was compatible with the spirit of a "New South," eager to resume relations with the North and to attract new commerce and industry. Newspaper editor, Henry W. Grady, promoted the New South, especially emphasizing the need to re-shape an economy which, as the Civil War had demonstrated, was too dependent on agriculture. Italianate designs prevailed into the early postwar period, but by the seventies new styles, such as Second Empire and High

Victorian Gothic, appeared in public and business buildings and began to influence residential styles. Elements like mansard roofs on otherwise Italianate houses, gables and pinnacles in business buildings, and wood scrollwork for residential porches signaled the change. Building technology was also changing, slowly in a slowly-recovering economy, but iron columns appeared more frequently on the street fronts of shops at ground level, and the city's first passenger elevator was built into the Kimball House in 1870. Architect William H. Parkins set up his office in the mid 1860s, was joined by Alexander C. Bruce in 1879, and hired the first architectural draftsman in the city, Thomas H. Morgan, that same year.

Union Passenger Depot II, Maxwell V. D. Corput, 1870-1871. **Railroad Tracks between Pryor Street and Loyd Street (later renamed Central Avenue). Demolished 1930. Photograph, Atlanta Historical Society Collections.**

In the confusion of the immediate post-Civil War years, a temporary wooden structure served as a railroad station, but by the early seventies recovery was sufficient to support the building of a new iron shed on the central site previously occupied by the antebellum structure. A new iron trussed shed with a roof of corrugated galvanized iron was constructed by the J. P. Stidham Co., later known as the Philadelphia Architectural Iron Company. In the company's catalogue for 1872 a drawing and description of the Atlanta structure was offered to inspire future clients. Engineers Corput and Bass apparently drew the design which adorned, but did not obscure, the iron shed. Mansard roofed towers of varied profile were picturesquely arranged above rows of Italianate arches.

23

Buildings to serve the needs of the railroads were among the earliest to be rebuilt after the war. They were strung along the tracks throughout the central district. Originally three stories high and crowned with a cupola, this Italianate building was a landmark of the rebuilding city. This structure, like most nineteenth century buildings, served mixed functions. Offices for railroad officials, a large meeting room which served as a city concert hall, and sleeping quarters for traveling railroad officials were incorporated into the modest office portion in front of long loading docks. Because of a fire in 1935, only a one-story fragment remains attached to a rebuilt loading section.

Essentially intact near the Georgia Railroad Depot is the Freight Depot of the Atlanta & West Point Railroad, built about the same time, also in the Italianate style. Architecturally one of the most interesting buildings surviving in the central area, the building incorporates well-handled details. Stone and wood trim and cast iron window pediments on scroll brackets give it architectural distinction. Once a large number of freight depots and railroad service buildings were strung along the tracks throughout the central district. This fine structure is now one of only three remaining nineteenth century railroad structures in the central district.

Georgia State Capitol Building I, William H. Parkins, 1869. **Southwest corner Marietta and Forsyth streets. Burned 1893. Photograph, Atlanta Historical Society Collections.**

The state government was moved to Atlanta from Milledgeville in 1869. Legislative meeting rooms and official offices were quickly incorporated into the half-finished shell of a building begun as an opera house by the controversial postwar entrepreneur, Hannibal I. Kimball. The French Empire style mansard roof above an Italianate facade provided an up-to-date image—a fitting expression of the young Reconstruction city's newly established position as seat of the state government.

Kimball House I, William H. Parkins, 1870. **Pryor Street between Wall and Decatur streets. Burned 1883. Photograph, Atlanta Historical Society Collections.**

Kimball's first hotel was another expression of the young city's confidence. A mansard-roofed, French Empire design, six stories high, it was the largest hotel in the South and boasted both the city's first passenger elevator and first central heating system. Visitors were greeted in a luxurious lobby with a variegated marble floor, a fountain, and tropical plants. The lobby was open to galleries through the first three floors. Travelers to the city were awed by the substantial bulk of this building which, it is reported, served to guide them through the welter of confusing streets and railroad tracks in the center of the city.

Grant Building I, architect unknown, 1871. Southeast corner Marietta and Broad streets. Demolished 1910. Photograph, Atlanta Historical Society Collections.

Atlanta businessmen of the early 1870s used a relatively consistent Italianate style for their buildings. It introduced a common uniform pattern in the rather confused milieu of the postwar city. Italianate blocks with regularly spaced and capped windows, horizontal string courses, and overhanging cornices were based on a palazzo form. They were popular with American merchants who recognized their symbolic connections to an Italian merchant aristocracy. This Grant Building was the first of many to bear the name of an Atlanta family active in real estate development through several generations.

U. S. Post Office and Custom House, William A. Potter, 1878. 55 Marietta Street. Demolished 1930. Photograph, Atlanta Historical Society Collections.

With this structure both the presence of the federal government and the work of its architect, William A. Potter, made an impressive showing in the city. Potter, who followed the more well-known A. B. Mullet as Architect of the Treasury, supplanted his predecessor's preference for the Second Empire style with High Victorian Gothic which he also used for federal buildings in several other cities. This seems to have been the earliest Atlanta example of the bold Victorian version of the Gothic style.

Grant Building II, William H. Parkins, 1876, later Ivan Allen-Marshall Building. Demolished 1964. Photograph, Atlanta Historical Society Collections.

While the Post Office was under construction, local architect Parkins tried his hand with elements of the new style. With its bracketed eaves and round arched window pattern, the second Grant Building resembled earlier business blocks. But its multiple gables and banded window caps introduced High Victorian elements. For a brief period in the 1880s a future president of the United States, Woodrow Wilson, like many young men of the day attracted to the growing city of Atlanta, maintained a law office in this structure.

Healey Building I, William H. Parkins, 1877. Northwest corner Marietta and Peachtree streets. Demolished 1930. Photograph, Atlanta Historical Society Collections.

In the first Healey Building, with its elaborate bracketed cornice, variegated segmental window arches and busy surfaces, Parkins' firm used features of the High Victorian style more boldly. The local press pronounced the building "quite modern looking." Like the Grants, members of the Healey family were active real estate developers and builders.

27

North Hall, William H. Parkins, 1869. **Atlanta University, now Gaines Hall of Morris Brown College. 643 Hunter Street. Photograph, courtesy Historic Preservation Section, Georgia Department of Natural Resources.**

North Hall, the first building of Atlanta University, stands as a monument to the beginning, in the early post Civil War period, of one of the country's most important black educational institutions. Built of brick with segmental arches, bracketed eaves, and classical doorway detailing of the Italianate architecture characteristic of the period, it was an early Atlanta design of William H. Parkins.

Chrisman Hall, architect unknown, 1877. **Clark University, McDonough Boulevard. Burned 1934. Photograph, Atlanta Historical Society Collections.**

Eight years after North Hall was built, a second institution of higher learning for black citizens was established in Atlanta in a building whose general form was influenced by earlier Italianate buildings. The bold central tower with its unusual combination of roof and eave elements was an assertive statement of the importance of such institutions to the community.

Shrine of the Immaculate Conception, William H. Parkins, 1869-1873. 48 Hunter Street. Photograph, Atlanta Historical Society Collections.

The antebellum weatherboarded structure of 1848 which preceded the present Shrine of the Immaculate Conception on this downtown site was the first Catholic Church in Atlanta. Its pastor, Father Thomas O'Reilly, is widely known in the city as the figure who was influential in saving this earlier building and surrounding structures from burning in 1864. Yet, within five years the parish undertook the construction of a new large church above the muddy streets and destruction of the postwar city. Its continuing presence in the downtown district is remarkable. Architect Parkins combined features and qualities of several versions of the Gothic style. Plain brick walls and pinnacled square towers were derived from early nineteenth century English buildings. Interior details and composition reveal French and Italianate influence. In combination, they create an austere, yet picturesque building.

First Presbyterian Church, architect unknown, 1878. **95 Marietta Street. Demolished 1916. Photograph, Atlanta Historical Society Collections.**

Like commerical structures, church buildings too showed the developing taste for picturesque variety by the end of the 1870s. The entrance tower here is asymmetrically placed on one corner and the roof cap is a mansard shape; but the eaves line, as in the earlier Chrisman Hall, is jagged. Multiple gables and pinnacles, banded and pointed arches, and vigorously detailed brick and stone surfaces display typical features of the High Victorian Gothic style. By this time the style was appearing frequently on downtown streets.

The modest structure, derived from New England prototypes, which had housed the congregation of the First Presbyterian Church since antebellum days thus gave way toward the end of Reconstruction to a much more assertive High Victorian building.

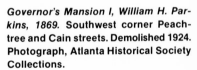

Governor's Mansion I, William H. Parkins, 1869. **Southwest corner Peachtree and Cain streets. Demolished 1924. Photograph, Atlanta Historical Society Collections.**

The first governor's mansion was designed as a private residence for banker John H. James who had come to Atlanta barely twenty years earlier as a $10-per-week store clerk. Architect William H. Parkins planned an elaborate arrangement of reception rooms, parlors, a carriage porch, glass conservatory, stable, laundry, ice house, cistern, and servants' quarters. In the year following its completion, it was sold to the State of Georgia. The masses of the house, boldly angled to either side of a tall central tower and connected by a veranda, must have been impressive on a prominent ridge on Peachtree Street, where the Peachtree Plaza Hotel now stands. Details included windows with assorted headings, two-story bay windows, and varicolored slate roofs and wooden scrollwork. The building was a mixture of design elements which the local newspaper pronounced "a style that may be called American, though ... mixed with the French and Gothic."

James W. English Residence, architect unknown, c. 1871. 40 Cone Street. Demolished 1925. Photograph, Atlanta Historical Society Collections.

The site of this typical brick residence of the period is now the center of the business district. When James English, a banker, built it, the business center was several blocks to the south, and the streets unpaved. It was English who, after he became mayor in the early 1880s, was instrumental in having the central city streets paved with Belgian block.

George Hillyer Residence, William H. Parkins, 1877. 31 Crew Street. Demolished 1950s. Photograph, Atlanta Historical Society Collections.

The Hillyer residence displayed features typical of the more substantial houses of the Reconstruction period. Of brick, with well-defined rectangular masses, square tower, and rambling verandas, the Italianate design included eaves brackets, segmental arched window caps, and vigorously modeled wooden trim.

31

More typical of early postwar residential architecture were smaller, frame buildings like this cottage. Judging from extant photographs, the raised cottage plan was probably unusual, but the modest scale and simple detailing were not. The casual reference to the Gothic Revival in the low pointed arches of the porch was also typical of this period when a mixture of styles was popular and Italianate buildings were becoming more common.

Later and larger, this residence was built for Col. Reuben Arnold outside the city limits and later sold to Jack J. Spalding. It was similar to the Lynch residence in its material and detailing. A two-story frame structure with high triangular roofs and gables, rambling one-story veranda, decorated with wooden cutwork and eaves brackets, it was an Italianate country house not unlike those promoted at mid-century by the widely-read Andrew Jackson Downing in *The Architecture of Country Houses.*

THE ELEGANT EIGHTIES

1880-1891

Roof-top View of Atlanta looking northwest from the State Capitol Building in 1889. **Photograph, Atlanta Historical Society Collections.**

Atlanta's International Cotton Exposition of 1881 heralded a period of growth and prosperity. Promoting industrial development in a "New South," the exposition was housed in an interesting Greek-cross-shaped building designed by G. L. Norrman. The building later served as a cotton mill. An influx of 28,124 new citizens swelled the city population by 1890 to more than 65,000 persons; the city limits were enlarged, the muddy streets paved, and gas street lamps replaced by electric lights.

Business buildings grew taller, intruding upon the steepled skyline. Railroad tracks, in an ever widening band, continued to dominate the center of the bustling city. Large business blocks took over former central city residential space, but the downtown functioned still as a mixed-use district where many shopkeepers and workers lived above and behind the new buildings. The multi-story, mixed-use block predominated. Some merchants built domestically scaled shops below upper story residential units. Most residences, large and small, spreading out from this center were built on individual lots rather than in the rowhouses and large tenements more common in northern cities.

Architects' offices increased in number, and the development of the profession was encouraged by the launching in 1889 of an Atlanta-based journal, *The Southern Architect and Building News.* Picturesque-eclectic High Victorian styles prevailed for all building types and were an appropriate expression for a young city working to establish itself as a regional center. Large building projects of the decade vigorously asserted the city's optimism and vitality.

33

Kimball House II, L. B. Wheeler, 1884-1886. **Pryor Street between Wall and Decatur streets. Demolished 1959. Photograph, Atlanta Historical Society Collections.**

This splendid hotel structure, according to a contemporary observer-was "a mixture of the Old Dutch, the Renaissance, and the Queen Anne style. It [was] very much broken, and yet every part [was] in perfect harmony with every other part and the whole combined [made] one of the grandest buildings in this country." The building was uniquely possible in this period which admired a rich mixture of materials and had access to both new technology and to craftsmen skillfully trained in the old traditions.

Exterior walls of rough stone masonry were pierced by iron piers at intervals to provide shop windows along the street facades. Advancing and receding upper wall surfaces of brick and terra cotta were elaborated with pressed metal ornament. Window openings and building elements were composed asymmetrically in a variety of ways. Projecting bays and a *porte-cochere* were topped with stepped and scalloped gables. Polished oak wainscoting, tiled floors and fireplace openings, carved woodwork, polished brass filigree screens, and marble stairways created a rich melange of interior details. The ground floor lobby, open through seven floors to a skylight and surrounded by galleries at each floor, was a delightful garden swept by refreshing breezes that was "simply beyond imagination," according to a nineteenth century observer. The Kimball House thus provided a local precedent for the open, sky-lighted lobby of the recent Hyatt-Regency House.

34

Atlanta Constitution Building, L. B. Wheeler, 1883-1885. **Southeast corner Alabama and Forsyth streets. Demolished 1967. Photograph Atlanta Historical Society Collections.**

The architect for both the Kimball House and this building arrived in Atlanta in 1884 to open an office with the Atlanta businessman, H. I. Kimball. In this second of his Atlanta buildings, Wheeler continued to show his preferences for plastic wall surfaces and asymmetrical articulation of elevators accented by a corner turret in which curved panes of glass provided wide windows.

Steps led into the building's main entrance under a granite pediment carrying the name and date of the building on large scroll brackets. Grotesque heads of granite formed the keystones for two large semicular arches enclosing subsidiary arches and wide windows in the Alabama Street facade. Terra cotta panels of flat ornament and molded chimneys added to the typically rich mixture of materials: heavy timbered mill construction, occasional iron posts and beams, and masonry walls. Oiled pine wainscoting and pressed metal ceilings were the major interior features.

The Atlanta Constitution, one of the city's oldest newspapers, built this five-story structure only eleven years after it outgrew a building constructed as recently as 1873. The growth of the paper and its move into a second building, especially constructed for its use, were indications of the growth of the city during this decade.

35

Moore-Marsh Building, Fay and Moser, 1881, later Haverty's Store. Northwest corner Edgewood Avenue and Pryor Street. Demolished 1974. Photograph, Atlanta Historical Society Collections.

Both the synthetic, creative eclecticism of the period and the characteristic use of natural forms as sources for ornament were displayed in this impressive building. The polychromy and verticality of the High Victorian Gothic style were combined in typical Atlanta fashion with arched windows and brackets of Italianate derivations. The decoration of pilaster caps and horizontal banding was derived from such natural forms as cotton bolls, corn, wheat, and sunflowers.

Moore-Marsh Building interior. Photograph, courtesy Haverty's.

Built for a wholesale dry goods company, this interior boasted iron columns with floriate capitals. They were the first structural columns cast in Atlanta by the Atlanta Machine Works—tangible evidence of the city's growing industrial capabilities.

Fulton County Courthouse, Parkins and Bruce, 1881-1883. **Southwest corner Pryor and Hunter streets. Demolished 1911. Photograph, Atlanta Historical Society Collections.**

This courthouse, built by Fulton County "to serve forever the needs of the county," was demolished in 1911 to make way for the present larger and more monumental structure. It was one of the few designs of the firm of Parkins and Bruce. Alexander C. Bruce came from Knoxville. Tennessee, in 1879 to join the office which Parkins had established in 1864. Bruce brought with him a portfolio of his designs for county courthouses in Tennessee. This Second Empire building, very different from previous Parkins work, is possibly a Bruce design. Boldly picturesque, the composition of projecting elements, Italianate arches and moldings, multiple gables, and mansard roofs was built up to a tall clock tower at the street intersection.

Gate City National Bank Building, G. L. Norrman, 1883-1884. Southwest corner Alabama and Pryor streets. Partially demolished 1929. Photograph, Atlanta Historical Society Collections.

This multi-story structure gave evidence of the commerical growth and prosperity of the 1880s. Not a multi-purpose block, it was an office building with lower floor banking spaces. It was one of the earliest designs of G. L. Norrman, an important late nineteenth century Atlanta architectural figure.

In typically High Victorian fashion, rough masonry and round-arched Romanesque Revival windows were combined with gables, balustrades, and Greek motifs. The variety in window shapes and sizes and the mixture of surface materials were features of the Queen Anne style which the architect used widely in his early work.

Georgia State Capitol Building, Edbrooke and Burnham, of Chicago, architects, 1884-1889. Washington Street between Hunter and Mitchell streets. Photograph, Atlanta Historical Society Collections.

After Atlanta was affirmed as capital of the state by special election in 1879, a new and, it was said, sufficiently imposing building was constructed to house the government. A special commission held an architectural competition and chose a style considered appropriate to the dignity and authority of government. The capitol building's architectural vocabulary was classical, but the vertical thrust of its tall dome and the complexity of its massing mark it as a forcefully Victorian building. The capitol was significant not only as the embodiment of a young city's now firmly established position in the state, but also because it played an important role in the city's building industry.

The Capitol Commissioners called in a consulting architect from New York City, George B. Post. He had pioneered with iron construction in that northern city, and he advised the use of a fire resistant iron and masonry construction. Miles and Horn of Toledo, Ohio, the contractors whose bid was within the one million dollar budget demanded by the legislature, moved their offices to the city. Their subsequent influence on the construction industry here was, according to a prominent contemporary Atlanta architect, significant. The gold leaf for the dome is of recent origin, delivered to Atlanta in 1958 by wagon train from the historic North Georgia gold mining community of Dahlonega. It was a gesture that would have pleased the Victorian Atlantans who served on the Capitol Commission. The commissioners tried to complete the building exclusively with Georgia materials but were unsuccessful because the construction industry here at the time was underdeveloped.

Hebrew Orphanage, G. L. Norrman, 1888. **478 Washington Street. Demolished 1974. Photograph, Atlanta Historical Society Collections.**

A Near Eastern theme was undoubtedly considered appropriate to this building because it was planned for a Hebrew organization. Norrman's design for this structure displays influences from Byzantine and Islamic architecture. The tall minaret-like clock tower and the additional towers and turrets were capped by onion domes. Horseshoe arches and flat, lacy ornament reinforced the theme, and textural richness was created by carefully detailed terra cotta ornamental blocks and columns in the brick walls.

Stone (Fountain) Hall, G. L. Norrman, 1882. Old Atlanta University
Campus, now Morris Brown College. 643 Hunter Street. Photograph,
courtesy Historical Preservation Section, Georgia Department of
Natural Resources.

Recently designated a National Landmark, Stone Hall stands on an
elevated point in Atlanta and has long served as a beacon of higher
education for America's black citizens. The three-story, red brick, High
Victorian building with its large round arched entranceway, tall two-
staged clock tower, and contrasting stone window sills and lintels em-
bodies the courage and determination that created and maintained the
early university.

40

Rockefeller Hall, architect unknown, 1885. Spelman College Campus, 350 Spelman Lane. Photograph, courtesy Historic Preservation Section, Georgia Department of Natural Resources.

Rockefeller Hall is the earliest of several interesting nineteenth century buildings on this campus. With its surface elaboration of brick patterning and pigmented headers and its cavernous Syrian arched entranceway and cupola of ornamented wood, it has been the center of campus life from the early days of the college.

Staff Row, Fort McPherson, architect unknown, 1880s-1890s. Photograph Atlanta Historical Society Collections.

Like the Atlanta University Center District, Fort McPherson preserves a fascinating complex of High Victorian architecture. Some two-family structures, together with monumental dwellings for high ranking officers, were built in brick with terra cotta detailing. They stand facing the spacious parade ground.

41

Ballard Institute, John Moser, 1882. 141-143 Peachtree Street. Demolished 1920s. Photograph, Atlanta Historical Society Collections.

Designed by John H. Moser for Mrs. Josephine Ballard's Atlanta Female Institute, this building faced Peachtree Street with a three-story veranda vigorously elaborated with cut-woodwork ornament. Lingering Italianate influence could be seen in the arched window caps, but pointed arches in the narrow third story gallery and multi-colored banding introduced elements of the High Victorian style. After 1892 when the school closed in the wake of competition from other private girls' schools, and just in time for the influx of visitors to the Cotton States Exposition, Mrs. Ballard converted her building; it became the Ballard Hotel.

St. Philip's Episcopal Church, Fay and Moser, 1881. Northeast corner Washington and Hunter streets. Demolished 1930s. Photograph, Atlanta Historical Society Collections.

In Fay and Moser's design for a church structure, the unique features of High Victorian Gothic style were evident. This multi-colored building replaced the simple, Early Victorian Gothic frame building which had served St. Philip's congregation before the Civil War. The wide proportions of the facade were somewhat atypical, although a steeple that was planned but never built would have provided verticality characteristic of the period.

St Luke's Episcopal Church, G. L. Norrman, 1883. Corner Pryor and Houston streets. Demolished 1906. Photograph, Atlanta Historical Society Collections.

The churches of this period were beginning to move away from the city center to the residential areas around its edges. St Philip's was located on its original site in an area that by the end of the decade was dominated by the new state government building, but St. Luke's was built north of the center, one block off Peachtree, in a residential area. Its convex curved pyramidal tower roofs were unusual. Also unusual was its Palladian window — a rather early Atlanta example of this motif which in America was usually associated with Georgian Revival buildings.

43

**Big Bethel African Methodist Episcopal Church, architect unknown,
1891. 220 Auburn Avenue. Photograph, of a drawing in E. R. Carter,
The Black Side, Emory University, Special Collections.**

In 1921 fire damaged Big Bethel Church, one of the key landmarks in
the Sweet Auburn Historic District. Therefore, the building no longer
retains its High Victorian appearance. As designed c. 1890 for the African
Methodist Episcopal Association, it was a splendidly bold Romanesque
Revival design. Round arched openings in the gray granite walls were
emphasized with moldings; a conical roof in the lower west turret
contrasted with the pyramidal roof and round-arched, open belfry atop the
taller square east tower. The high hipped roof over the meeting house
sanctuary was capped by a conical roofed lantern. With its lower walls
intact, the building remains an impressive monument to the significant
social and religious role it has played in the Auburn Avenue community
since the nineteenth century.

George Winship Residence, architect unknown, early 1880s. 481 Peachtree Street. Demolished 1936. Photograph, Atlanta Historical Society Collections.

The multiple mansard roofs of the George Winship residence were old-fashioned earmarks of the Second Empire style at the time the house was built. However, the contrasting stone trim of the hood molds over the rectangular windows was characteristic of developing High Victorian styles. So, too, were the heavier, bolder eaves brackets and elaborately carved wooden porch details. The styles of the 1870s continued to influence residential architecture as Atlanta's businessmen built houses like this along Peachtree Street and other streets leading northward from the city's center.

Joel Chandler Harris Residence, "Wren's Nest," architect unknown, c. 1885. 1050 Gordon Street. Photograph, Atlanta Historical Society Collections.

The home of writer Joel Chandler Harris, now maintained as a museum by the Joel Chandler Harris Memorial Association, is a nice example of the smaller frame, suburban residence of the early and mid-eighties. Situated in West End, once a fashionable suburb, the two-story house appears low and rambling under steeply pitched multiple roofs. Additions and remodeling of a simpler earlier structure by Harris soon after moving here in 1881 produced the typical picturesque outlines and richly ornamented surfaces of the period. Notable details include fish scale shingles in second story facade and porch gable and the wooden lattice arches under the porch eaves.

Julius Brown Residence, Bruce and Morgan, 1885. **140 Washington Street. Demolished 1957. Photograph, Atlanta Historical Society Collections.**

The Julius Brown residence was the first recorded work of a new and subsequently important local architectural office, that of Bruce and Morgan. The house was built in a stylish residential area which was called "Capitol View" after 1889 when the new Georgia State Capitol was built just north of the neighborhood. The massive square block of this symmetrically composed building was unusual in a period characterized by the asymmetry associated with the Queen Anne style. But the use of a combination of features from at least two architectural styles was more typical of the period: round arches derived from the Romanesque and window bandings like those used in High Victorian Gothic buildings.

Edward C. Peters Residence, G. L. Norrman, 1883. 179 Ponce de Leon Avenue. Standing as The Mansion Restaurant. Photograph, Atlanta Historical Society Collections.

The Peters house, now adapted to comtemporary use as a restaurant, is Atlanta's finest example of the Queen Anne style residence. The style was characteristic of the most fashionable residences in High Victorian Atlanta. The general features of the style — asymmetry of massing and a mixture of materials and details — appear here together with variations appropriate to Atlanta's climate — for example, the deep porches. The precise, sometimes classical details, half-timbered gables, scalloped wooden shingles, terra cotta ornament, and molded chimneys are typical of the American version of this style which originated in England. Triangular, terra cotta ornaments, used instead of wooden shingles as transition elements between the stories, are unusual. Possibly they were products of a local terra cotta works active through the later nineteenth century in Atlanta, Pellegrini and Castleberry. Interior detailing survives, including wooden lattice-work, panels of a wallpaper fashioned to resemble tooled leather, and tiles in the dining room fireplace decorated with scenes and symbols from the Peters family's original home city, Philadelphia. Both in its architectural form and interior details the house incorporates references to the family's Philadelphia ancestry.

47

Milledge Bates Residence, Bruce and Morgan, 1890. 701 Peachtree Street, Demolished 1911. Photograph, Atlanta Historical Society Collections.

The irregular massing, multiple gables, and complex silhouette are typical features of the Queen Anne style. So-called "Eastlake" turned posts, curved brackets, and spool-work were often added to such buildings. The round corner gazebo integrated into a long veranda was apparently used widely in Atlanta for both large residences and smaller cottages.

Clarence Knowles Residence, L. B. Wheeler, 1890. 13 Ponce de Leon Avenue. Demolished 1950. Photograph, Atlanta Historical Society Collections.

The shingle style, which was an American outgrowth of the approach to composition and form developed in the Queen Anne style, was at one time widely evident along Atlanta's streets. In this house by one of the most influential architects working in the city during the 1880s, the salient features of the style can be seen. A uniform layer of shingles covers the surfaces of the multiple facades; multiple roofs and gables intersect as in the Queen Anne style but the composition is more horizontal. Ground story walls are of rough masonry; and windows of a variety of shapes and sizes have small panes.

Eberhart Residence, architect unknown, 1880s. Oak Street. Demolished 1975. Photograph, Atlanta Historical Society Collections.

The one-story Victorian cottage, sometimes with hipped roof, sometimes with A-line roof, but always with a projecting gable oriented to the street, was a familiar building type for modest houses of the 1880s and 1890s. With their ample verandas open to the street, such structures helped to create interesting and distinctive neighborhoods for the less affluent of both races in Atlanta. Although urban renewal programs in the late 1950s and 1960s cleared away many such neighborhoods, some streets lined with this characteristic frame architecture remain on the west side, in and around the Martin Luther King, Jr., Historic District and in south Atlanta.

Aaron Perry Residence, architect unknown, 1880s. Haynes Alley. Demolished 1960s. Photograph, E. R. Carter, *The Black Side,* Emory University Special Collections.

49

Joseph Thompson Residence, architect unknown, c. 1890. **Peach-tree Street, Brookwood. Demolished 1960s. Photograph, Atlanta Historical Society Collections.**

Joseph Thompson lived in a suite of rooms in the Kimball House Hotel. This was his summer home in Brookwood, just north of the Southern Railway's Peachtree Station. This example of the shingle style included a roof swept down from the ridge to cover an open porch. So-called eyebrow dormers, also common to the style, were low and incorporated into the roof surface. The overall effect here was simpler, quieter, and more horizontal than in the Queen Anne style.

A View of the Cotton States Exposition. **Photograph, Atlanta Historical Society Collections.**

In the mid-nineties Atlanta had the audacity, only thirty years after Sherman had ravaged the town, to invite the world to a fair. It was planned as an antidote to hard times. This Cotton States and International Exposition provided a platform from which the city announced her position as distribution center for the Southeast.

The buildings of the fair revealed attitudes about architectural styles in a landscaped setting. The site later became a city park. The majority of buildings were frame structures, designed by consulting architect Bradford Gilbert of New York, to utilize native Georgia materials and local craftsmen. The Fine Arts and Woman's exhibits, however, were housed in monumental structures designed in the Beaux-arts classical style, the style which would prevail in the early twentieth century city.

These buildings displayed to the throngs of visitors who came to Atlanta in 1895 the confidence of the young city. The commerical and social growth which allowed the city to advertise itself through the fair had been developing throughout the post-Civil War years. In the nineties, it peaked in two major building events: Atlanta's first skyscraper office building (Page 55) and her first planned and landscaped residential suburb (Page 52). Both were prophetic of future patterns of growth. Such developments provided visible evidence of the end of the Victorian era and the beginning of the modern city. Yet, both suburb and skyscraper were very much the outgrowth and expression of the Victorian age, of its technology and attitudes toward architectural forms.

Inman Park, a suburb developed by the East Atlanta Land Company, Joel Hurt, President, 1887. Photograph, Atlanta Historical Society Collections.

Inman Park was Atlanta's first planned residential suburb, developed by Joel Hurt as a part of a larger plan which included a street railway and a modern office building. Hurt, a civil engineer, supervised the construction of this picturesque residential area, laying out the curving streets after the fashion of Frederick Law Olmsted and hiring a landscape gardener, Joseph Johnston, to plan green spaces and gardens. Hurt pushed through a new city street, Edgewood Avenue, to make a straight-line connection with the site of his proposed office building downtown. He engineered one of the country's first electric street railways to provide rapid transit from Inman Park to town.

Inman Park Street Car Barn, architect unknown, c. 1890. 963 Edgewood Avenue, N. E. Photograph, Atlanta Historical Society Collections.

The Car Barn for the street railway, one of the few remaining shingle style buildings in Atlanta, is a visible reminder of this earlier mode of transportation.

**View of Edgewood Avenue, Inman
Park.** Residences, 1890-1895. **Photograph, Atlanta Historical Society Collections.**

Along the streets of the suburb in the
late nineteenth and early twentieth centuries, Atlanta's newly successful businessmen built boldly modeled and elaborately detailed houses. Several along
Edgewood Avenue were photographed
in 1895 and are shown here.

**John M. Beath — John R. Dickey Resi-
dence, architect unknown, c. 1898. 866
Euclid Avenue. Photograph, Atlanta
Historical Society Collections.**

The Beath-Dickey residence, in which
the present restoration of the suburb began, was one of the first houses
built in the neighborhood. Asymmetrical,
turreted and incorporating a mixture of
material in the manner of Queen Anne
style, it was set in the landscape in
a fashion typical of the period.

Equitable Building, Burnham & Root of Chicago, architects, 1891-1892, later Trust Company of Georgia. **Northeast corner of Pryor Street and Edgewood Avenue. Demolished 1971. Photograph, Atlanta Historical Society Collections.**

At the town end of the street rail-line from Inman Park the South's pioneer skyscraper, the Equitable Building, was opened in 1892. Its designer was a native son, John Wellborn Root, who grew up in Atlanta before the Civil War. Sent from the wartime city to school in England, Root eventually joined Daniel H. Burnham in Chicago in an architectural partnership which contributed to the creation and development of the skyscraper building form.

Root's Atlanta building, planned just prior to his untimely death in 1891, was similar in several ways to his Rookery Building of 1884-1886 in Chicago. It is possible that entrepreneur Joel Hurt had seen the earlier Chicago building. Like its predecessor, the Equitable's exterior street facades were of self-supporting brick and stone masonry and were enriched with terra cotta ornament. The building's steel framed construction was evident in the lighter brick and terra cotta infilling of its court walls. Richly textured interior details included marble wainscoting, wrought iron elevator doors, and an eight-story stairway. A steel and glass skylight covered the banking room in the court.

The general populace was at first fond of calling this massive building "Hurt's Folly." Yet, the building was a success both as a work of art and as an economic venture. As its promoter had predicted, business firms looking for a southern location moved to Atlanta and rented space in the building. By the time the Cotton States and International Exposition was planned, the success of the Equitable Building was evident.

Rear court wall of Equitable Building, Burnham and Root of Chicago, architects, 1891-1892, later Trust Company of Georgia. Demolished 1971. Photograph, collection, Elizabeth A. Lyon.

Stairway in Equitable Building, Burnham and Root of Chicago, architects, 1891-1892, later Trust Company of Georgia. Photograph, collection, Elizabeth A. Lyon.

English-American Building, Bradford Gilbert of New York, architect,
1897, later Georgia Savings Bank, now Hamilton Bank Building.
74 Peachtree Street. Photograph, Atlanta Historical Society
Collections.

In the improved economic climate that followed the Cotton States
Exposition of 1895, Atlanta's businessmen began to invest in tall office
buildings. The first of these, and now the city's oldest standing example,
was the English-American Building. Blueprints, originally filed in 1896
with the new city building inspector's office and now owned by the
Hamilton Bank, give us the name of the architect, Bradford Gilbert of
New York. Gilbert was the supervising architect of the 1895 Exposition
and maintained an office in Atlanta during 1895 and 1896, but little
else is known about the planning stages of the building.

While land values in the central district were rising, construction
photographs of the building do not show a dense environment which
would have dictated such a narrow building. What these photographs do
emphasize, however, is the vigorous modeling of the facades, the poly-
chromed exterior surfaces, and the tall, narrow profile presented to view
at the intersection of two major downtown streets that make this building
a fine image of the optimism and expansiveness of Victorian Atlanta.
Because of its shape the building was known between 1916 and 1920
as the Flatiron Building. It actually predates New York's more famous
Flatiron Building by five years.

Prudential Building, Bruce & Morgan, 1898, later Grant Building, now Standard Federal Building. 44 Broad Street. Photograph, Atlanta Historical Society Collections.

This was one of the buildings which helped to establish the architectural reputation of Bruce & Morgan as a prominent Atlanta firm. The Austell Building of 1896-1898 (later Atlanta Journal-Constitution Building) had been the first tall office building of the partnership of Alexander Bruce and Thomas H. Morgan. For that earlier building, as well as for the surviving Prudential Building, the architects used ornament derived from Renaissance sources.

The composition of this second fully steel-framed building in Atlanta reflects the influence of the Chicago School. John W. Grant, the building's entrepreneur, sent the architects to Chicago during the planning stages of the structure to observe building practices in the city that had invented the steel-framed skyscraper. Wide, horizontally extended windows in the plain shaft of the Prudential Building reveal the influence of this trip. Bruce & Morgan's buildings earlier in the decade had been, by contrast, massive High Victorian designs.

Concordia Hall, Bruce & Morgan, 1893. Northwest corner Forsyth and Mitchell streets. Photograph, Atlanta Historical Society Collections.

The Concordia Society, founded in 1866 as a social and cultural organization, publicized plans for this picturesque structure in Morgan's *Southern Architect and Building News* in 1892. The building opened in 1893. Unlike another proposed Concordia Society building plan by E. G. Lind shown in an earlier edition of the journal, Bruce & Morgan's design included store spaces along the Mitchell Street facade. The doorway on Forsyth Street led to a concert hall and meeting rooms. That doorway, with a lyre in a broken scroll pediment and with elaborate terra cotta ornamentation referring to the literary and musical activities of the society, survives. The parapet walls, with their gables and pinnacles, and the projecting corner turret, topped by an onion-domed cupola, have unfortunately disappeared.

***Southern Bell Telephone & Telegraph
Building, G. L. Norrman, c. 1893.***
**Southwest corner Pryor and Mitchell
streets. Demolished early 1950s. Pho-
tograph, Atlanta Historical Society
Collections.**

High Victorian eclecticism gave way
briefly in the nineties to a new simplified
approach to commercial design associated with Chicago architects, which
historians now call "commercial style." It
was used not only in the skyscraper office
buildings but also in smaller business
buildings. In this Atlanta example of 1893
for the new southern headquarters of the
Telephone Company, G. L. Norrman uti-
lized a simplified overall form as well as
distinct features which originated in the
buildings of the early modern architect,
Louis Sullivan. Spandrels of the windows
grouped vertically under round arches
were inset, and small circular openings
in the top story were surrounded by the
luxuriant, flat patterned ornament developed by Sullivan. Later, about 1900, two
more bays were added to the east side
of the building, making a symmetrical
composition.

***Church of the Sacred Heart, W. T.
Downing, 1897-1898.*** **335 Ivy Street,
N. E. Photograph, courtesy Historic
Preservation Section, Georgia Depart-
ment of Natural Resources.**

The Church of the Sacred Heart stands
as an example of the innovative and
imaginative eclectic work of one of Atlanta's most interesting architects, Walter
T. Downing. In typical nineteenth century
tradition, he chose elements from several
centuries of Romanesque architecture—
towers, arches, corbel tables and moldings—and skillfully combined them into
a homogeneous and visually effective
design. Contributing to its richly textured
and ornamented quality are warm red
brick and terra cotta facades with marble
embellishment, marble interior floors,
terra cotta, iron columns, and generous
areas of stained glass windows. This re-
markably well-preserved building has been
the central structure serving a complex of
religious and educational activities since
the late 1890s when the Marist fathers
settled permanently in Georgia. Now surrounded by parking lots and commercial
structures, the site in 1897 was in a
residential area and criticized as too far
out from the city center.

William P. Nicolson Residence, W. T. Downing, 1891-1892. 821 Piedmont Avenue. Photograph, Atlanta Historical Society Collections.

Downing employed a formula typical of the period in the general composition of this house—two-story block under a hipped roof with asymmetrical porch and projecting wing. He freely adapted Renaissance and classical motifs, columns, pilasters, friezes, swags, and garlands to create a rich texture. Such houses signaled the return of a taste for classical designs which would become more intense under the influence of the Beaux-arts later in the decade. Downing's work is visually complex, yet often carefully orchestrated. Here the unifying shell motif is boldly announced on the exterior and continued into interior detailing.

William Greene Raoul Residence, Bradford Gilbert of New York, architect, 1892. 848 Peachtree Street. Standing behind later structure at 848 Peachtree Street. Photograph, Atlanta Historical Society Collections.

The rear and side facades of this once splendid mansion are now hidden behind later commerical facades on Peachtree Street. They are a rare reminder of the fine residences that once lined Atlanta's most famous thoroughfare. The house was designed by New York architect Bradford Gilbert, who later designed buildings for the Cotton States and International Exposition. Gilbert designed asymmetrical masses with varied window shapes and sizes, intersecting gable roofs and porches extending into spacious grounds. Though it is more horizontal than high Queen Anne designs, this substantial brick mansion displays features of the Queen Anne style which continued to shape Atlanta's residential architecture until the turn of the century.

Martin Luther King Birth Home, architect unknown, c. 1893.
**501 Auburn Avenue. Photograph, courtesy Historic Preservation
Section, Georgia Department of Natural Resources.**

While elaborate Victorian houses were going up in Inman Park and other
residential areas within the city, more modest frame dwellings in a modified Queen Anne style were being constructed in many Atlanta neighborhoods.

This two-story frame dwelling was built by the Holbrook family. It later
attained great historical significance as the birthplace of Martin Luther
King, Jr. It is typical of a residential style that was characteristic of many
early 1890s residential sections. Generous porches extended partially
along front and side facades. A projecting section with gable oriented
to the street provided a background for wooden fans and strapwork
decoration. Turned porch posts supported cut-woodwork brackets and
eaves boards. This nineteenth century neighborhood was originally
part of a larger area where there were no distinctly segregated residential
patterns. In the changed climate of the early twentieth century, the
neighborhood became the home for many of Atlanta's successful black
families.

Edgar P. McBurney Residence, W. T. Downing, 1892. 65 West
Peachtree Street. Demolished c. 1907. Photograph, Atlanta
Historical Society Collections.

Architect Downing was perhaps better known for his larger residences
in an array of well-handled eclectic styles, but he was also interested
in new ideas. This charming Shingle Style cottage was built for Edgar
P. McBurney, who later built a larger residence farther out from
town on Peachtree Street. The interesting composition of turret,
gables, masses, and porches was enhanced by the large, elephant-
ear leaves in a planting characteristic of the period.

TURN OF THE CENTURY

1900-1918

General View of Atlanta, 1903. Atlanta Historical Society Collections.

By the early twentieth century Atlantans looked at a cluster of new skyscrapers and proclaimed their rapidly changing city to be the "New York of the South." While the steel-skeleton technology was vigorously applauded, nineteenth century commercial-style was rejected in favor of more formal and often classical designs. Victorian asymmetry and picturesque forms gave way to symmetry and monumentality; mixed eclectic detailing to recognizably clear historical precedent. Conservative styles soon changed the overall context of business streets and dominated new residential streets. The architectural image was one of affluence and stability befitting, so it was thought, the established and succesful distribution center of the Southeast.

Terminal Station, P. Thornton Marye, 1904-1905. Northwest corner
Mitchell and Spring streets. Demolished 1971. Photograph, Atlanta
Historical Society Collections.

For the Terminal Station Marye pioneered in the use of a new material,
reinforced concrete, using it to build the wide-span enclosures of its
offices and waiting rooms. These structures, with the transverse skylights
in the sawtooth roof over the concourse, were built by the Baltimore
Ferro-Concrete Company in a manner that was close to a type of folded
plate construction not fully developed until the 1950s. The building
featured the last of the large all-covering train sheds built in the United
States. It spanned the tracks behind the station but was hidden by
a facade made up of Renaissance Revival arcades. Here, as in many
early twentieth century stations, the idea of the picturesque survived
in complex massing and multiple towers. The use of a grand and
monumental facade as an expression of the urban gateway was gaining
prominence at the time throughout the country. For Atlanta, dubbed
from its earliest years "the gateway to the South," this building design
must have seemed especially appropriate.

Terminal Station (interior view), P. Thornton Marye, 1904-1905. Photograph, collection, Elizabeth A. Lyon.

Carnegie Library, Ackerman and Ross of New York, architects, 1900-1902. 126 Carnegie Way, now Atlanta Public Library. Photograph, Atlanta Historical Society Collections.

The Beaux-arts Classical Revival arrived full force in Atlanta in this, the ninth library given to an American city by Andrew Carnegie. The design of a New York City firm was chosen in a competition over those submitted by Atlanta architects W. F. Denny and W. T. Downing who won second and third places respectively. Paired monumental Ionic columns, generous round arched windows, and inscribed entablature under a modillion cornice were hallmarks of the style and no doubt considered symbolically suitable to a public building dedicated to culture. Subsequent remodeling has altered the once grand interior spaces, taken out the predimented window inserts, and removed the large stained glass window which is a part of the present exhibit.

All Saints Episcopal Church, Bruce and Morgan, 1903. **Northwest corner North Avenue and West Peachtree Street. 634 West Peachtree Street. Photograph, courtesy Historic Preservation Section, Georgia Department of Natural Resources.**

While the Gothic Revival styles were deemed appropriate to religious buildings over a long span of time, during the early twentieth century, the interpretation of Gothic historical precedent was more "correct" and less creative than during the High Victorian era. Here the red-brown tones of the building stone added warmth to forms which had become more academic.

First Baptist Church, G. L. Norrman, 1906. **209 Peachtree Street. Demolished, 1929. Photograph, Atlanta Historical Society Collections.**

An example of Late Victorian Romanesque Revival, this was one of the last known works by this prolific High Victorian architect. The heavy, rough surfaced gray granite structure, contrasts strongly with many of Norrman's earlier elaborate, eclectic buildings. It was part of a new stylistic trend in tune with the more single-minded eclecticism of its day. Identified by contemporary reports as Norman Gothic, the massive structure demonstrated a design approach that was gaining popularity—reliance on a single identifiable stylistic precedent.

First Congregational Church, Bruce and Everett with Pharrow Construction Company, 1908-1909. **105 Courtland Street. Photograph, courtesy Historic Preservation Section, Georgia Department of Natural Resources.**

Built to replace the original early Gothic Revival frame structure which had served Atlanta's black community since 1867, this generally Renaissance Revival building is enlivened by Spanish Baroque elements that were unusual in Atlanta church buildings. Richness has been added to the traditional meetinghouse interior space by a full complement of stained glass windows said to have been made at a nearby shop.

Empire Building, Bruce and Morgan, 1901, now Citizens and Southern National Bank. **35 Broad Street. Remodeled 1929, Hentz, Adler and Shutze. Photograph, Atlanta Historical Society Collections.**

This ten-story building was the second Bruce and Morgan skyscraper to show the strong influence of the architects' study trip to Chicago in the late 1890s. Originally its steel-skeleton construction was covered rather simply with buff brick and terra cotta piers and recessed spandrels, and its base story opened behind wide glass panels. The classical motifs of its modest ornament, however, not only reflected changing contemporary tastes, but betokened future changes. In 1929, when the Citizens and Southern Bank remodeled the building for its main offices, the three stories of the base were filled with Renaissance Revival stone facades and the interior turned into one of the grandest spaces in downtown Atlanta. To many people it is the epitome of a great banking hall.

Century Building, Bruce and Morgan, 1901-1902, now Atlanta National Bank. Northeast corner Alabama and Whitehall (renamed Peachtree Street South) streets. Photograph, Atlanta Historical Society Collections.

Bruce and Morgan moved more strongly toward classical design in this early office building constructed for George W. Scott, textile mill owner and founder of Agnes Scott College. The grandly scaled entranceway which once dominated this important, nodal intersection has been obliterated by later remodeling. But there remain interior details common to office buildings of the period such as the wrought iron stairway open through several floors and some ornamental brass hardware.

This interesting early skyscraper has just been given a three-year reprieve from the wrecker's ball. Rapid rail line builders must preserve the building while seeking feasible plans for adaptive renovation and use.

Healey Building II, Bruce and Morgan and Walter T. Downing, 1913. 57 Forsyth Street. Photograph, Atlanta Historical Society Collections.

Walter T. Downing was apparently the major designer for this later and atypical Atlanta skyscraper. Acclaimed by many Atlanta architects as the best of the early skyscrapers, its antecedents were clearly Gothic Revival. Gothic details ornament the unusual projecting first story shop windows, the cornice edges, the ribbed elevator lobby ceiling, and interior court space originally intended as a connection to a second tower portion that was never built. Downing, who constantly experimented in his buildings with a variety of formal elements, created here an effectively simple office tower slab.

Candler Buiding, George Murphy and George Stewart, 1906. 127 Peachtree Street. Photograph, courtesy Historic Preservation Section, Georgia Department of Natural Resources.

A "Twentieth century business palace" was what contemporary admirers called this early eighteen-story building.

Built according to the desires and specifications of Asa G. Candler, founder of The Coca-Cola Company, it is the paramount example of Victorian individualism carried into the twentieth century. Lavishly faced in Georgia marble, its facades were covered by elaborate carvings executed by a crew of Italian carvers under the direction of a sculptor named F. B. Miles who assured contemporary Atlantans that the sculpted images "stood for something." Around the base stories are panels dedicated to everything from agriculture to the liberal arts. Inside, overlooking the monumental stairway, reside historical Georgia figures like Alexander Stephens and Mr. Candler's parents. A carved dolphin on the newel post adorns stairs that lead to a basement where an elaborate bath establishment was originally housed—placed there for the comfort of building tenants.

69

Third National Bank, Walter T. Downing with Morgan and Dillion, 1911, now Atlanta Federal Savings Building. 20 Marietta Street. Refaced in 1962. Photograph, Atlanta Historical Society Collections.

W. T. Downing's first commission as associate architect with Morgan and Dillon was originally a traditional three-part composition of base, shaft, and capital into which he inserted yellow terra cotta ornament. Downing told a younger architect working in his office at the time that he was trying to "invent a style." It is clear that "style" meant dropping obvious historical precedent and substituting the recessed window spandrels and the vigorous overhanging cornice.

George Muse Building, architect unknown, 1902. 7 Whitehall Street (renamed Peachtree Street South). Demolished c. 1922. Photograph, Atlanta Historical Society Collections.

Little is currently known about this interesting structure other than what can be seen in this photograph. The recorded image, however, reveals a building with a predominantly glass facade and with light, filigree detailing, both of which were unusual features for buildings in Atlanta and most other cities of the period. It is a facade that can be compared in its transparency and detailing with a later building in San Francisco, the acclaimed Hallidie Building of 1918.

Odd Fellows Building and Auditorium, William A. Edwards with Pharrow Construction Company, 1912-1913. **250 Auburn Avenue. Photograph, courtesy Historic Preservation Section, Georgia Department of Natural Resources.**

Built to serve the needs of Atlanta's black community during a period of intensified segregation, these two structures are impressive statements of community strength. The six-story office building and adjacent auditorium-theatre building were cast in a modified Jacobean-Commercial style and elaborated with carved stone and terra cotta figures in a manner that was common during the period. These figures, however, with their recognizable features are an effective and early expression of community pride and consciousness.

Detail, Carving, Odd Fellows Building and Auditorium. **Photograph, courtesy of Historic Preservation Section, Georgia Department of Natural Resources.**

Rich's Department Store, Morgan and Dillon, 1907. **82 Whitehall Street (re-named Peachtree Street South). Photograph, courtesy Historic Preservation Section, Georgia Department of Natural Resources.**

Morgan and Dillon's remodeling of Rich's store, like the Muse's facade, suggests the influence of commercial style buildings associated with the Chicago School. Wide areas of glass were created here by windows grouped in threes between uninterrupted vertical piers. These were separated by recessed balcony panels of iron filigree work.

Eiseman Buiding, Walter T. Downing, 1901-1902. **47-49 Whitehall Street (re-named Peachtree Street South). Demolished 1976. Photograph, Atlanta Historical Society Collections.**

The formula used by Downing in this Beaux-arts Renaissance Revival facade for the Eiseman Clothing Company was becoming more prevalent on early twentieth century commercial facades. Elaborate ornamentation and classically derived details, put together here with great sophistication by the architect, were a strong part of the later commercial streetscape.

Sadly, these fine facades and neglected interior spaces with their stylishly ornamented iron columns and pressed metal ceilings, were in the path of the new rapid transit line.

Peachtree Arcade, A. Ten Eyck Brown, 1916-1917. 2 Peachtree Street. Demolished 1964. Photograph, Atlanta Historical Society Collections.

Looking to historical precedent for the Renaissance Revival facades and to new technology for its interior steel and glass roof, Architect Brown summed up in this building the dichotomy of early twentieth century Atlanta architecture. Atlanta's businessmen and developers have long taken pride in their progressive skyscrapers and commercial structures with conservative Beaux-arts classical facades. This early twentieth century shopping center, which stood for only forty years, was a light-filled and exciting space in downtown Atlanta.

Interior, Peachtree Arcade. Photograph, Atlanta Historical Society Collections.

73

In this finely executed example of neo-Georgian classicism by noteworthy Atlanta architect Neel Reid, the new and more academic approach to historical precedent was applied to a small suburban railroad station. Built to serve a growing suburban residential community, it is now Atlanta's only remaining passenger railroad station.

A. G. Rhodes Residence, W. F. Denny, 1904, now Annex for Georgia State Archives. 1516 Peachtree Street. Photograph, Atlanta Historical Society Collections.

This massive granite Romanesque Revival residence was built between 1901 and 1904 for the A. G. Rhodes family. Modeled, it is said, after several Rhineland castles, the design was executed by W. F. Denny, a turn-of-the-century Atlanta architect, who died at an early age not long after designing this building.

The mansion on 100 acres was originally associated with the development of the Ansley Park residential area. Later, an early shopping center known as Rhodes Center was built on opposite sides of the single block now occupied by the mansion, and later commerical developments along Peachtree Street separated the house from the residential neighborhood.

The Rhodes Building, now owned by the state, was the gift of the A. G. Rhodes family in the 1930s to house the state Department of Archives and History. Before the archives moved to a new building in 1966, the family donated the staircase with stained-glass windows to the state for preservation in the new archives, where they are on display to the public. The windows were designed as a memorial to the Confederacy.

Robert Maddox Residence, architect unknown, 1911. **391 West Paces Ferry Road, site of the present Governor's Mansion. Demolished 1966. Photograph, Atlanta Historical Society Collections.**

A former mayor, Robert Maddox, in 1911 built a Tudor style country house on his estate facing West Paces Ferry Road. It started the development of the larger surrounding area as a fashionable residential area of large houses designed in styles of specific historical periods. During subsequent years the Tuxedo Park Company, founded in 1911 by Charles H. Black, subdivided several tracts in the area into large building lots and developed curving driveways to serve them. The Maddox home, like many others here, was originally a summer house, but as automobiles became more common and the inner areas of the city more crowded and commercial these houses became permanent residences.

J. Carroll Payne Residence, architect unknown, 1908. **Southwest corner of Peachtree and Fourth Streets. Demolished 1960s. Photograph, Atlanta Historical Society Collections.**

A good example of the widespread Classical Revival style of the period, the J. Carroll Payne house with its monumental columned portico, was built in the suburban community of Brookwood.

Alonzo Herndon Residence, architect unknown, 1909. 587 University Place. Photograph, courtesy Historic Preservation Section, Georgia Department of Natural Resources.

Throughout the city large mansions as well as more middle-class houses were built in recognizable period styles for Atlanta's successful citizens. The founder of one of the nation's most prestigious black financial institutions, the Atlanta Life Insurance Company, built this fine Beaux-arts classical mansion just five years after the company was established. Alonzo Herndon began his career as owner-operator of Herndon's Tonsorial Palace in central Atlanta and became one of the city's most respected citizens.

William Alanson Gregg Residence, G. L. Norrman, 1903. 176 Capitol Avenue. Demolished 1957. Photograph, Atlanta Historical Society Collections.

In one of his later residential designs, Architect Norrman provided an example of the changing taste in a frame dwelling. Like many of his earlier and more modest residential buidings, the general composition was made up of picturesque and asymmetrical masses. Roof lines and ornamentation were quieter, and detailing showed the influence of classical traditions. Such houses were regarded as 'colonial" in feeling if not exact in form.

William J. Stoddard Residence, architect unknown, c. 1915. Piedmont Road. Photograph, Atlanta Historical Collections.

Probably the most characteristic house type for Atlanta dwellings of modest scale built between 1910 and the First World War was strongly influenced by the English-born Arts and Crafts Movement. The "Craftsman" style, popularized by Gustav Stickley in his nationally distributed magazine, *The Craftsman*, was most often used for one or one-and-a-half story bungalows, and could also be found in two-story residences. Common elements of these designs were broad gables, stick-style brackets, shed roof dormers, and porch posts on masonry pedestals. Often shingles were applied, at least to the upper portions of the the buildings.

EPILOGUE

The taste for the creative eclecticism of the late nineteenth century was overwhelmed by the turn-of-the century preference for classical and other clearly recognizable period styles. Succeeding generations have continued to admire buildings like Brookwood Station which were based on historical precedents in the classical style. This twentieth century taste has contributed to a lack of concern about Atlanta's nineteenth century heritage.

Such an attitude was in tune with national trends in which Beaux-arts architectural imperialism and academically correct period buildings were preferred. This taste has been particularly long-lived in Atlanta. Classical and Neo-Georgian styles referred to the late eighteenth and early nineteenth centuries and were popularly associated with the architecture of the Old South. Atlantans have assumed that these buildings and furnishing styles represented their city's heritage. This belief has contributed to the destruction of Atlanta's Victorian architecture. Ironically, the loss of this earlier architecture was hastened by a characteristically Victorian premise: "Tear it down, and build it bigger and better," an approach identified proudly by a local writer in 1929. This idea of progress was a basic theme of the Victorian era.

Atlantans have embraced both academic revival styles and the idea that new buildings are necessarily better buildings with the result that very little remains of a once-rich nineteenth century heritage. "Anything new will look better down there at Five Points," a letter writer to the newspaper observed in 1959 when the Kimball House was coming down. The grand old building was replaced by a concrete and enameled aluminum parking garage. While many links to the culture from which present-day Atlanta grew have been obliterated by such natural disasters as fire, most have been systematically destroyed in the rush of new development.

This is a tragic loss, for as New York *Times* architectural critic Ada Louise Huxtable once observed, the form of an historic structure is " . . . a moment in time, crystallized as style." Through the styles of our historic structures we can not only enjoy a visually rich and varied environment, but can see and appreciate the culture which created our present way of life. Such a dialogue with the past is present only rarely in Atlanta's environment. While there are residential neighborhoods in which there are enough structures extant to preserve a sense of time and place, much of the city gives the appearance of having been built only yesterday.

Occasionally, as in the Atlanta Life Insurance Company district for example, more than one decade of development remains. Together in one block at Piedmont and Auburn Avenue stand buildings representing one of Atlanta's oldest businesses, the John Smith Carriage Factory (c. 1890—the company is now the John-Smith Chevrolet Company), and one of the nation's most significant black financial institutions, the Atlanta Life Insurance Company (facades 1927, 1939). Nearby is the city's first black office building, the Rucker Building (1906). Also standing here are the homes of carriage maker John Smith (c. 1872) and of Henry Rucker (1860s), who built the early twentieth century office building. In structures spanning more than fifty years, the older and typical Atlanta patterns of mixed living and working are visible.

The old downtown district in which Underground Atlanta is located also preserves nineteenth century patterns and a characteristic streetscape. This area will be severely damaged by a much-needed transit system. Ironically, rapid transit was an integral part of late nineteenth century development. Only fragments of historic Atlanta will be visible in the new system and much will be destroyed.

Atlanta has been slow to recognize the role which historic buildings can play in the urban environment. Buildings preserved as museums, such as the Wren's Nest, home of writer Joel Chandler Harris, and the Martin Luther King, Jr., Birth Home, where the internationally influential civil rights leader was born and spent his early childhood, are important. Houses from two very different periods of Atlanta's development, the plantation plain-style Tullie Smith farmhouse of about 1840, and the Palladian Revival Swan House of 1928, are preserved on the grounds of the Atlanta Historical Society. Atlanta's several historic house museums provide opportunities to experience some of the life styles of the past or provide touchstones to the lives of significant individuals. But in addition to such relatively isolated museums, the city needs historic buildings which function as living pieces of their urban environment.

When the Kimball House was replaced by a parking garage, not only did Atlantans lose a richly-detailed structure and a former center of community life, they also lost a rare opportunity to adapt an historic showplace into a new kind of urban attraction. It is sometimes possible to renovate old buildings and return them to their original uses. This has been done in neighborhoods like Grant Park and Inman Park, and in business buildings like the Hamilton Bank. More often, in order to preserve old buildings, we must adapt them to new uses. Most nineteenth-century buildings have been neglected and ignored in plans for new developments in Atlanta. Yet many gems have survived, needing good architectural renovation combined with restoration. Buildings like the Atlanta and West Point Freight Depot, the Raoul residence, the Peters House, the Hosch and Son Store building which became the first Coca-Cola bottling plant—now the Baptist Student Center—and the Carnegie Library deserve and need new and creative treatments.

They present exciting challenges to concerned citizens willing to work out adaptive and profitable uses for the neglected or under-utilized spaces within these now faded shells. They can and should function effectively in today's economy. Until very recently, Atlantans have not recognized the economic potential of the city's older buildings, nor placed much value on their continued existence.

Atlanta aspires to status as an international city, but all such great centers reveal their histories in their man-made environments. The variety that is present in such cities produces distinct and recognizable places which attract and hold residents and businesses because of their special characteristics. We must meet the challenge to preserve and enhance Atlanta's Victorian heritage in the context of the vigorous contemporary city.

SELECTED OBJECTS IN THE EXHIBITION

Tin panel, ornament from exterior of Kimball House Hotel, 1883-1885. Collection of Mrs. Bruce Montgomery.

Carved granite medallion from the Silvey Building, architect unknown, 1912. Corner of Spring and Marietta Streets. Collection of Hudgins and Company, Inc.

*Rendered elevation of Kimball House Hotel, North facade along
Decatur Street, L. B. Wheeler, 1883-1885.* Original drawing, Atlanta
Historical Society Collections.

Window showing fruit, collection of Mr. and Mrs. William Mann.

Window showing hares and doe, collection of Mr. and Mrs. John H. Merritt.

Terra cotta ornament from Kimball House Hotel, Lorenzo B. Wheeler, architect, 1883-1885. Terra cotta made by Pellegrini and Castleberry, Atlanta.
Collection of Mrs. Bruce Montgomery

Panel with stylized foliate motifs, collection of Mr. L. M. Becknell.

Four terra cotta blocks with leaf and flower motifs from the Julius Brown residence, Thomas H. Morgan, 1885. 159 Washington Street.
Collection of Mr. and Mrs. Andrew Sparks.

Column assembly and ornamental wall blocks from Hebrew Orphanage, G. L. Norrman, 1888. 478 Washington Street. Demolished 1974. Collection of Continental Wrecking Company.

Edward C. Peters Residence, G. L. Norrman, 1883. 179 Ponce de Leon Avenue. Standing as The Mansion Restaurant. Watercolor sketch by the architect, Atlanta Historical Society Collections. The gift of the estate of Lucile Kuhrt Peters.

*Terra cotta finial in the shape of a bell from a tower of Terminal
Station, P. Thornton Marye, 1904-1905.* Northwest corner Mitchell
and Spring streets. Collection of Mr. and Mrs. Bealy Smith.

Bird's eye view of the Cotton States and International Exposition, lithographed by the Werner Co., Akron, Ohio, 1895. Lithograph, Atlanta Historical Society Collections.

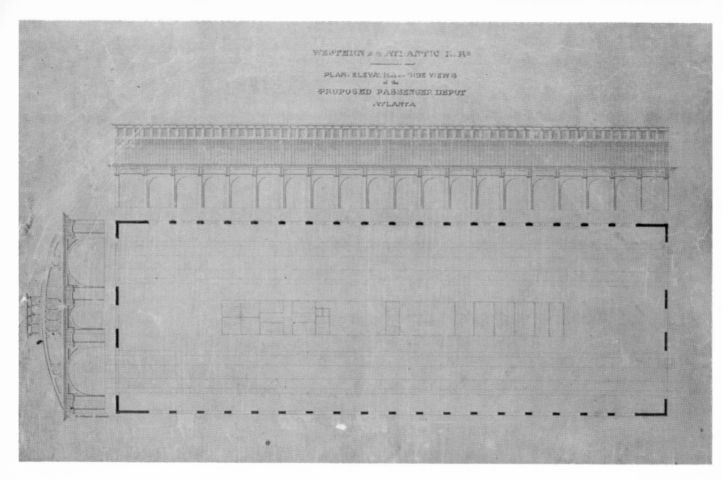

Plan and elevations for the "Passenger House," Edward A. Vincent,
1852-1854. Demolished by Federal Troops in 1864. Original drawing,
Atlanta Historical Society Collections. The gift of Laura Armstrong.

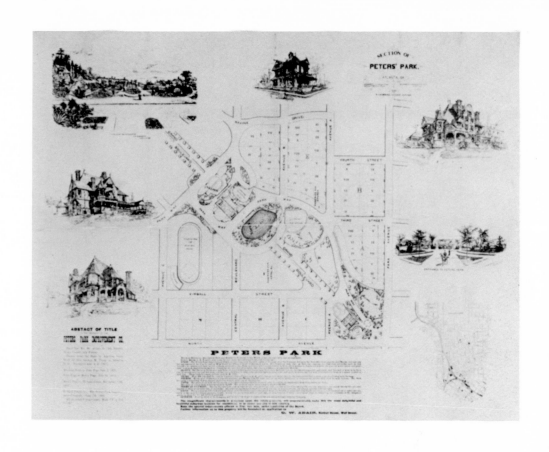

Peter's Park plan, lithographed map with cuts showing houses for a proposed residential development of H. I. Kimball and the architect L. B. Wheeler with the real estate firm of G. W. Adair. Little of the project was executed on the site now occupied by Georgia Tech. Lithograph, Atlanta Historical Society Collections. The gift of Mrs. Albert S. Anderson, Jr.

John H. Moser's suggestion of a facade for the A. I. A. Building,
from the "American Architect and Building News," Jan. 19, 1884.
Courtesy of Southern Technical Institute Library.

Doorway fragment from Atlanta Constitution Building, L. B. Wheeler, 1883-1885. Southeast corner Alabama and Forsyth streets. Demolished 1967. Collection of Mr. and Mrs. Bealy Smith.

Carved granite ornament from Luckie Street School, Haralson Bleckley, 1910. Corner Luckie and Pine streets. Collection of Hudgins and Company, Inc.

Proposed plan for Bleckley Plaza, Haralson Bleckley, 1909. Only the viaducts were built. Original drawing, Atlanta Historical Society Collections.

APPENDICES

I. MAJOR ATLANTA ARCHITECTS

INTRODUCTORY BIOGRAPHIES

JOHN BOUTELL

(b. 1814: Active here 1852-1883: d. 1886)

THE FIRST ATLANTAN
TO CALL HIMSELF "ARCHITECT"

After arriving from Massachusetts, Boutell was one of three "Architects and Builders" listed in Atlanta's first City Directory of 1859. After the Civil War the directories listed him as "builder," "carpenter," or "contractor." Though not a formally-trained architect, he was responsible for architectural designs in modified Greek Revival and Italianate styles, doubtless derived from builders' guides and other pattern books.

ALEXANDER C. BRUCE

(b. 1835: Active here 1879-1904: d. 1927)

ATLANTA'S FIRST MEMBER OF THE
AMERICAN INSTITUTE OF ARCHITECTS

PARTNERSHIPS

1879-1882 Parkins and Bruce (W. H. Parkins)

1882-1904 Bruce and Morgan (T. H. Morgan)

Born in Fredericksburg, Virginia, Bruce trained in the Nashville, Tennessee, office of an English architect, H. M. Akeroid. In 1864 he began his own practice in Knoxville and in 1873 was elected to associate membership in the American Institute of Architects. He came to Atlanta in 1879 to form a partnership with W. H. Parkins, and the two participated in designing many public buildings in Georgia. In later partnership with T. H. Morgan, he was responsible for business buildings in High Victorian Gothic, Renaissance, Romanesque, and other revival styles, as well as buildings in the more utilitarian "Commercial Style."

WALTER THOMAS DOWNING

(b. 1865: Active here 1880s-1918: d. 1918)
STYLISH RESIDENTIAL ARCHITECT
OF THE TURN OF THE CENTURY

Downing's widowed mother brought him here from Boston when he was a child, and he grew up in this city. He studied architecture as an apprentice to L. B. Wheeler. A late Victorian eclectic, Downing leaned heavily toward classical styles, with which he experimented, handling plans and details in an inventive manner. He also designed in Tudor, Gothic, and other styles. Though some public buildings are among his works, the most impressive bulk of his production took the form of houses for affluent Atlantans in which the interiors were elaborately detailed.

PARTNERSHIPS

1889-1890 Wheeler and Downing (L. B. Wheeler)

1910-1914 Worked in Association with Morgan and Dillon on several buildings.

P. THORNTON MARYE

(b. 1872: Active here 1904-1935: d. 1935)

Born in Alexandria, Virginia, in 1872, P. Thornton Marye entered the University of Virginia in 1889. He began the practice of architecture in 1892 in Newport News, Virginia, and was working in Washington, D. C., when he drew the plans for Atlanta's Terminal Station. He opened his office in the city in 1904 during the time his station was under construction. Marye thus began his Atlanta practice with a transitional building, one which used advanced construction techniques in a form which continued the intricacy of Victorian design. He later assumed the leadership of a large organization which planned and executed buildings throughout the southern states in a range of early twentieth century revival styles. Marye is perhaps best known for the Fox Theatre designed in 1928 in partnership with Richard E. Alger and Oliver J. Vinour.

PARTNERSHIPS

1904-1919 P. Thornton Marye

1920-1921 Marye and Alger (Barrett Alger)

1922-1925 Marye, Alger and Alger (Barrett and Richard W. Alger)

1926-1929 Marye, Alger and Vinour (Richard W. Alger and Oliver J. Vinour)

1930-1935 Marye, Vinour, Marye and Armistead (Oliver J. Vinour, J. Nisbet Marye, J. Warren Armistead, Jr.)

THOMAS HENRY MORGAN

(b. 1857: Active here 1879-1930: d. 1940)

FOUNDING PRESIDENT ATLANTA CHAPTER OF THE AMERICAN INSTITUTE OF ARCHITECTS

PARTNERSHIPS

1882-1904 Bruce and Morgan (A. C. Bruce)

1904-1919 Morgan and Dillon (John Robert Dillon)

1919-1930 Morgan, Dillon and Lewis (Edward S. Lewis)

Originally from Syracuse, New York, Morgan attended the University of Tennessee and stayed in Knoxville to begin in 1876 the study of architecture in the office of A. C. Bruce. He then studied with firms in St. Louis and New York. In 1879 he came to Atlanta as draftsman for Parkins and Bruce, then became Bruce's partner in 1882.

In 1889 he founded and edited a monthly architectural journal, *The Southern Architect*. He was founding president in 1906 of the local A.I.A. chapter. Abandoning the High Victorian forms of his earlier years, in his later work Morgan followed the trend of the times and relied on the classical forms popularized by the Beaux-Arts School.

GOTTFRIED L. NORRMAN

(b. 1846: Active here 1880-1909: d. 1909)

PARTNERSHIPS

1880-1882 Weed and Norrman

1883 Humphries and Norrman (G. P. Humphries)

1884-1907 G. L. Norrman

1908-1909 Norrman, Hentz and Reid (Hal Hentz, Neel Reid)

A native of Sweden, educated at the University of Copenhagen and at a German technical university, Norrman came to Atlanta after serving in the Swedish merchant marine and traveling in the American South. He designed several structures for the international expositions held in Atlanta in 1881 and 1887. His buildings ranged in style from Gothic and Romanesque Revival through exotic Middle Eastern fantasies to Queen Anne and the Shingle Style. In 1909 his architectural career ended in suicide.

WILLIAM H. PARKINS

(B. 1836: Active here 1864-1890: d. 1894)

ATLANTA'S FIRST POSTWAR ARCHITECTURAL OFFICE

A native of New York and Union sympathizer, Parkins was living in Columbia, South Carolina, at the outbreak of the Civil War. He fled northward but moved back South to Atlanta in 1864 to found the first postwar architectural firm here. It produced some of Atlanta's finest High Victorian buildings in Gothic, Second Empire, and Italianate Revival styles. His firm also designed a number of public buildings throughout Georgia.

PARTNERSHIPS

1871-1875 Parkins & Allen (J. Warner Allen)

1879-1882 Parkins & Bruce (A. C. Bruce)

1885-1886 Kimball, Wheeler & Parkins (H. I. Kimball, L. B. Wheeler)

1886-1887 Wheeler & Parkins

1888-1890 W. H. Parkins

NEEL REID

(b. 1885: Active here 1909-1926: d. 1926)

A FOUNDER OF ATLANTA'S MOST PRESTIGOUS EARLY BEAUX-ARTS FIRM

Neel Reid was educated in his hometown, Jacksonville, Alabama, until 1903 when he moved to Macon, Georgia, with his family. After completing high school and beginning an apprenticeship in a Macon architect's office, the young man came to Atlanta in 1904 to the office of W. F. Denny. With his future partner, Hal Hentz, Reid then went to the Columbia University's School of Architecture and from there to the *Ecole des Beaux-arts* in Paris. Both men returned to Atlanta in 1909 and joined briefly with G. L. Norrman to practice as Norrman, Hentz and Reid. From November, 1909, after Norrman's death, the young architects continued together to work in the changing architectural climate which was well suited to their training and temperaments. Reid, the principal designer of the firm in the pre-World War I years, developed considerable skill in a variety of classically inspired revival modes. His work was beginning to attract national attention within the profession at the time of his premature death. Upon his death a young man who had been a draftsman in the firm before studying abroad under the coveted Rome prize, Philip T. Shutze, became the principal designer continuing the preference for classical and Renaissance Revival styles which was the firm's trademark.

PARTNERSHIPS

1909 Norrman, Hentz, and Reid (G. L. Norrman, Hal Hentz)

1909-1912 Hentz and Reid

1913-1926 Hentz, Adler and Shutze (Hal Hentz, Rudolph Adler, Philip T. Shutze)

LORENZO B. WHEELER

(b. 1854: Active here 1883-1890: d. 1899)

HIGH VICTORIAN ARCHITECT FROM NEW YORK

PARTNERSHIPS

1883-1885 H. I. Kimball, L. B. Wheeler, and Co.

1885-1886 Kimball, Wheeler and Parkins (W. H. Parkins)

1886-1887 Wheeler and Parkins

1887-1889 L. B. Wheeler

1889-1890 Wheeler and Downing

Immediately after the fire that destroyed the first Kimball House Hotel in 1883, Atlanta entrepreneur H. I. Kimball went into partnership with this New York architect to build a bigger and better Kimball House. Wheeler arrived in January of 1884 with plans already prepared. The highly eclectic and picturesque character of the "Dutch Renaissance" hotel was typical of his designs in many styles. Henry Grady particularly admired his designs for interiors, and other contemporaries felt he revolutionized Atlanta architecture.

Wheeler remained in Atlanta for nearly seven years, residing in the Kimball House. His library there provided sources for his own designs and strongly influenced the work of his successor, W. T. Downing.

II. TERRA COTTA IN ATLANTA'S ARCHITECTURE

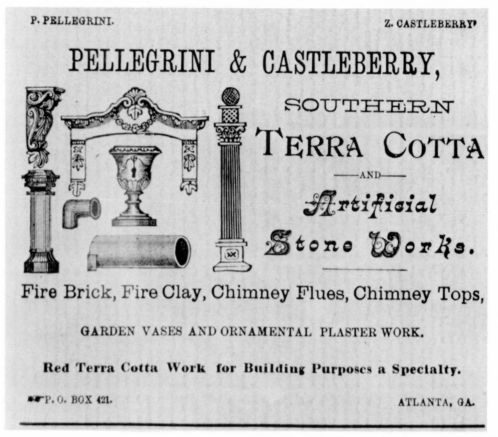

Pellegrini and Castleberry advertisement from The Southern Architect, March, 1892. **Photograph, Atlanta Historical Society Collections.**

Terra cotta ornaments added richness, texture, and interest to much of Atlanta's Victorian architecture. Ornaments of clay, formed in molds, then dried and kiln-fired, had been occasionally used by European architects from an early period, as well as by American architects like James Renwick of New York who used them during the 1850s.

In the 1870s, English architects, working in the "Queen Anne" style, popularized red brick buildings featuring decorative terra cotta panels molded in relief. The style caught on in America after English examples were greatly admired at Philadelphia's Centennial Exposition of 1876. Though popularized as features of red brick Queen Anne architecture, terra cotta ornaments were soon being substituted for carved work in buildings of Classical, Gothic, and all the array of late nineteenth-century styles. They were made by factories that sprang up all over the country during the 1880s and 1890s.

Local clays determined the color of terra cotta. Most of the earlier pieces of the seventies and eighties were cast in brick red clays, but the use of buff and white clays, often glazed, increased in popularity through the turn of the century. All of the examples in this exhibition were salvaged from Atlanta buildings. Much of this terra cotta was locally made.

Atlanta boasted one of the earliest and most widely-renowned manufactories of architectural terra cotta. It was started by Pellegrino Pelligrini in 1871. Zack Castleberry soon joined him to form the "Southern Terra-Cotta Works" with a factory in East Point. The curator and director of Philadelphia's Museum and School of Industrial Arts, Edwin A. Barber, writing in 1891 noted:

> Their architectural work, for exterior and interior decoration, is of a superior character. Some of their terra-cotta panels, supported by female figures, and their fireplace and chimney panels are especially meretorious.

After the departure of Castleberry in 1893 and of Pellegrini in 1897, the Southern Terra-Cotta Works continued in business until 1912.

GLOSSARIES

I. ARCHITECTURAL STYLES

The styles most frequently used in Atlanta's nineteenth and early twentieth-century buildings are briefly described. Until very late in the period, seldom was an Atlanta building constructed in a pure style. Rather, elements from several styles were often combined.

1890-1930

Although initially inspired by English design reformers, this was America's first native Modern Architecture. Departing from historical references, it emphasized use of natural materials, hand craftmanship, and expression of structure. Largely a residential architecture, houses featured broad overhangs, sleeping porches, and a deliberately simple, unpretentious character. A movement more than a style, it spawned varying expressions, some specifically regional—like the bungalow style of California, and the Prarie School style of the Midwest. More general interpretations derived from Gustave Stickley's *Craftsman Magazine* were built in Atlanta.

ARTS and CRAFTS

BEAUX - ARTS
Classical

1895-1930

Monumental, formal, classically detailed buildings strongly influenced by the *Ecole des Beaux-arts* in Paris. Symmetrical plans determine forms. Academically "correct" versions of classical orders and detail, rectangular windows, pedimented porticos, figural sculpture; grand scale and colossal columns. McKim, Mead and White the most famous American practitioners of the style. Hentz, Reid, and Adler used it most effectively in Atlanta.

BEAUX-ARTS Renaissance Revival

1895-1930

Monumental, formal, classically detailed buildings strongly influenced by the *Ecole des Beaux-arts* in Paris. Symmetrical plans determine forms. Round arches, horizontal moldings, regular window patterns, arcaded fronts, enriched surfaces; grand scale and colossal columns. McKim, Mead and White the most famous American practitioners of the style. Hentz, Reid and Adler most effectively used it in Atlanta.

1890-1930

Ornamentation is subordinated to wide rectangular windows in regular patterns within framing that reflects the steel skeleton construction of these early skyscrapers. Flat roof lines. Usually a base of one or two stories is set off from a tall shaft which is capped by a one or two story top and overhanging cornice. Chicago School skyscrapers provided American precedent for the early Atlanta skyscraper designers, Bruce and Morgan.

COMMERCIAL STYLE

Gothic Revival

1820-1860

Characterized by steep, pointed gables, pointed arches, pinnacles, battlements, window tracery and symmetrical or asymmetrical plans and massing. The use of pierced curvilinear ornament on eaves, barge boards, and porch roofs of these frequently wooden buildings began the fashion for "gingerbread" made with jig or scroll saw. Source: A. J. Downing's books on residential architecture popularized the style. Atlanta architects used the style infrequently for complete buildings, but did use elements from it mixed with other styles, as well as quantities of fancy-cut wooden ornament.

1820-1850

Formal, symmetrical buildings, often simple rectangular blocks with low-pitched roofs, and regularly spaced openings. Classical orders used for temple-front porticos and colonnades. Sources: Greek buildings as interpreted in pattern books of Asher Benjamin, Minard Lefever and others who modified the forms for American uses. The style was used in Atlanta by John Boutell.

GREEK REVIVAL

1870-1890

Standard Gothic elements—pointed arches, pinnacles, turrets, and tracery—used in bold and picturesque ways dramatized by strong variegation in colors and materials. Complex roof lines, towers, and generally top-heavy effects. Details heavier than those of the earlier Gothic Revival. Sources: English architect William Butterfield, Americans Edward T. Potter, William Ware. William H. Parkins and A. J. Bruce used this style for important downtown Atlanta buildings.

High Victorian Gothic

ITALIANATE

1840-1875

A domestic and commercial style earmarked by arched windows, bracketed eaves, and corner quoins, often used in combination with classical columns and pilasters. Early Italian villas usually were asymmetrical in plan and included low square towers. Some had bay windows, balustraded balconies, verandas, and large expanses of unadorned walls. Nearly flat pitched roofs topped these buildings. Sources: A.J. Downing, A.J. Davis. William Parkins and many anonymous designers of Atlanta business buildings used this style.

JACOBETHAN REVIVAL

1900-1930

Based on a combination of Elizabethan and Jacobean architecture, characterized by half-timbering, steep triangular or segmental gables that rise above roof lines, and rectangular windows divided into lights by thin mullions. Tall chimneys in clusters and turrets add verticality. "Tudor" residential buildings share many of these characteristics.

1900-1930

"Correct" interpretations of particular historical periods, usually constructed of monochromatic masonry or brick, simply detailed in stone. Used for churches and schools. Details of Gothic styles—cast in terra cotta—clad skyscrapers, emphasizing vertical lines.

LATE GOTHIC

1895-1930

Most popular among the classical styles adopted in Atlanta this eighteenth century revival was characterized by rectangular buildings with strictly symmetrical facades with crisp white detailing. Residences have one-story entrance porches, classically detailed eaves, windows and doorways, sometimes pediments over windows and often a Palladian window. Churches have entrance porticos and steeples that rise in several stages to a spire.

NEO - GEORGIAN

1876-1895

In America, this red-brick, English-born, and very free revival of early eighteenth-century English architecture was executed in many materials, including wood. Picturesque effects achieved in irregular plans and massing; rich variety in details. Windows of many shapes, multiple stepped and shaped Dutch gables, steeply-pitched roofs, and corner towers. Richly ornamented—much of the ornament abstract and unique in stylization—terra cotta panels, wooden gable fans, strapwork, turned spindles, and (on porches) bracketed posts. A simplified version here: two-story asymmetrical houses with gabled projections facing the street. Sources: red brick 1870s London buildings of Norman Shaw and W. Eden Nesfield. L. B. Wheeler and G. L. Norrman made effective use of the style in Atlanta.

1845-1880

Most used for straight symmetrical fronts under bold cornices of commercial buildings. In the Romano-Tuscan mode of the style; neutral walls, windows framed with moldings topped by lintels or flattened pediments, rusticated quoins. In more elaborate and later North Italian mode: windows arched, classical orders superimposed, one to each story. Sources: Italian palaces of High Renaissance. Popularized in America by John Nottman, by cast-iron producer James Bogardus, and others. Used in Atlanta by Alexander C. Bruce, T. H. Morgan, G. L. Norrman.

RENAISSANCE REVIVAL

1860-1900

Large rounded arches (frequently used over entrances), and rough stone masonry earmarks of the style. Bands of contrasting stone emphasize structural features—arches, lintels, and massive forms. Bandings and isolated panels of foliate and geometric ornament enrich stonework. Sources: early medieval architecture, first used in America during the 1840s by James Renwick and Richard Upjohn. In the 1870s Henry Hobson Richardson developed and personalized the style to attain international recognition for significant American architecture. Alexander C. Bruce and G. L. Norrman were among Atlanta architects who used the style, which persisted here until very late in the nineteenth century.

ROMANESQUE

106

1860-1880

High mansard roofs are the stylistic hallmarks of tall, boldly modeled buildings, frequently with dormers of many shapes, and with walls elaborated with pilasters and arches. Windows round headed or straight in regular patterns. Source: French buildings of the reign of Napoleon III (1852-1870). In America, Alfred B. Mullett's Treasury Building epitomized the style, sometimes called "General Grant." William H. Parkins and many local builders used it in Atlanta.

SHINGLE STYLE

1880-1900

Shingles cover walls, at least in upper stories, and often the entire structure. Horizontal emphasis in the massing of irregular forms, roof shapes, including many gambrel roofs, and towers. Sources: William Ralph Emerson, Henry Hobson Richardson, and McKim, Mead and White developed the style. G. L. Norrman, W. T. Downing and Thomas H. Morgan all used it in Atlanta.

107

GLOSSARIES

II. ARCHITECTURAL TERMS

Arcade — A range of arches supported on piers or columns attached to or detached from the wall.

Arch — Wedge shaped stones or bricks set in a curve.

Baluster — (Sometimes bannister) a turned or rectangular upright supporting a rail.

Balustrade — An entire railing system, as along the edge of a balcony.

Barge board — A stylized rafter set out from the clapboards of a gable.

Bay window — An angular or curved projection with windows.

Bracket — An overhanging member projecting from a wall, especially under the cornice, to support a weight.

Capital — The head of a column or pilaster.

Colonnade — A range or row of columns.

Column — A vertical support, round in section. In classical architecture the column has three parts, base, shaft, and capital.

Corbeling — A series of short stone, brick, or wood projections (corbels) supporting a projecting course of masonry.

Cornice — The uppermost, projecting part of an entablature or a feature that resembles it.

Cupola — A small dome structure rising from a roof or tower.

Cut-work — A type of pierced ornament made with jig-saw or scroll saw and much used in the Gothic Revival. Often popularly referred to as Gingerbread.

Dormer window — An upright window that projects from a roof and lights the space under the roof.

Eaves brackets — The name given to brackets, or overhanging support members under a cornice or eave.

Eclecticism — The selection and combination of elements from diverse styles.

Engaged column — A half-round column attached to a wall.

Entablature — Above columns and/or pilasters, a three-part horizontal section of a classical order, the topmost being the cornice.

Gable — The triangular upper part of a wall under the end of a ridged roof.

Half-timbering — A technique of wooden-frame construction in which members are exposed on the outside of a wall, used in the Victorian period as applied decoration.

Hipped roof — A roof with slopes on all four sides.

Hood-mold — A projecting molding above an arch, doorway, or window; also called dripstone molding.

Light — A section of a window, the pane, or glass.

Lintel — A beam over an opening in a wall, or over two or more pillars or posts.

Mansard roof — A roof with two slopes to all four sides, the lower being steeper than the upper.

Molding — A projecting strip of curvilinear profile on the surface of a building, or the curvilinear finishing of the edge of two meeting surfaces.

Order — A definite arrangement of column, capital, and entablature, each having its own set of rules and ornamental features: Tuscan, Doric, Ionic, Corinthian, Composite.

Palladian window — A group of three windows. The central opening is roundheaded and taller than the two flanking rectangular openings.

Pediment — A triangular space forming the gable of a two-pitched roof in classical architecture.

Pilaster — A flat-faced representation of a column, projecting from a wall.

Pinnacle — In Gothic architecture and derivatives, a small ornamental body or shaft terminated by a pyramid or spire.

Porte cochere — A carriage porch, or a doorway, large enough to allow a vehicle to pass through.

Portico — A large porch having a roof, often with pediment, supported by columns or pillars.

Quoin — One of the stones or bricks ornamenting the outside corner of a building.

Rustication — Rough surfaced stone work.

Segmental arch — An arch that is less than half a circle.

Spandrel — The portion of the wall that is directly below an upper story window.

Spoolwork — In contrast to the two-dimensional scroll-saw ornament, this type is distinctly sculptural and the product of the chisel, gouge, and lathe, in particular the name given to rows of spindles forming open work friezes along the porches, verandas, and in interiors.

String course — A projecting course of bricks or some other material forming a narrow, horizontal strip across the face of a building.

Syrian arch — A type of semi-circular arch with very low supports.

Tracery — Ornamental openwork of stone in the upper part of a Gothic window, either of wood or iron in Gothic Revival buildings.

Turret — A small slender tower.

Veranda — A space alongside a house sheltered by a roof supported on columns or posts.

SELECTED BIBLIOGRAPHY

Architectural Appreciation

Rasmussen, Stein Eiler. *Experiencing Architecture.* Cambridge, Mass., 1969.

Taylor, Joshua C. *Learning to Look.* Chicago, 1957; Cambridge, Mass., 1962.

Victorian Architecture and Technology

Andrews, Wayne. *Architecture, Ambition and Americans.* New York, 1947.

Condit, Carl. *American Building: Materials and Techniques from the First Colonial Settlements to the Present.* Chicago, 1968.

Early, James. *Romanticism and American Architecture.* New York, 1965.

Gifford, Don. *The Literature of Architecture: The Evolution of Architectural Theory and Practice in Nineteenth Century America.* New York, 1966.

Gowans, Alan. *Images of American Living: Four Centuries of Architecture and Furniture as Cultural Expression.* Philadelphia, 1964.

Hamlin, Talbot. *Greek Revival Architecture in America.* New Haven, 1944.

Hersey, George L. *High Victorian Gothic.* Baltimore, 1972.

Hitchcock, Henry Russell. *Architecture: Nineteenth and Twentieth Centuries.* Baltimore, 1958.

_____ *The Architecture of H. H. Richardson and His Times.* Cambridge, Mass., 1956.

Kaufman, Edgar Jr. *The Rise of an American Architecture.* New York, 1970.

Kidney, Walter. *The Architecture of Choice: Eclecticism in America 1880-1930.* New York, 1974.

Lynes, Russell. *The Tastemakers.* New York, 1954.

Maas, John. *The Gingerbread Age: A View of Victorian America.* New York, 1965.

Meeks, Carroll L. V. *The Railroad Station: An Architectural History.* New Haven, 1956.

Scully, Vincent. *The Shingle Style: Architectural Theory and Design from Richardson to the Origins of Wright.* New Haven, 1955.

Stanton, Phoebe. *The Gothic Revival and American Church Architecture.* Baltimore, 1968.

Whiffen, Marcus. *American Architecture Since 1780: A Guide to the Styles.* Cambridge, Mass., 1969.

Pattern Books

Bicknell, Amos Jackson. *Details, Cottage and Constructive Architecture.* New York, 1873.

_____ *Specimen Book of One Hundred Architectural Designs.* New York, 1878.

Bullock, John. *The American Cottage Builder.* New York, 1854.

[Dornsife, Samuel J., ed.] *Exterior Decoration.* Philadelphia, 1885; reprint ed., Philadelphia, 1975.

Downing, Andrew Jackson. *The Architecture of Country Houses.* New York, 1850; reprint ed., New York, 1969.

_____ *Rural Architecture and Landscape Gardening.* New York, 1842; reprint ed., Watkins Glen, N. Y., 1967.

Sloan, Samuel. *The Model Architect.* Philadelphia, 1852.

Vaux, Calvert. *Villas and Cottages.* New York, 1857; reprint ed., New York, 1968.

Current Journals

Historic Preservation.

Preservation News.

Journal of the Society of Architectural Historians.

Nineteenth Century.

Architecture and History in Atlanta

American Institute of Architects, North Georgia Chapter, ed., *Guide to the Architecture of Atlanta, 1975.*

Bacote, Clarence A. *The Story of Atlanta University.* Princeton, 1969.

Carter, E. R. *The Black Side.* Atlanta, 1894.

Connally, Thomas W. "Thomas Henry Morgan, Atlanta Architect 1879-1930." Seminar paper, Yale University, 1951.

Garrett, Franklin, *Atlanta and Environs.* 3 vols. New York, 1954.

_____ *Yesterday's Atlanta.* Miami, 1974.

Lyon, Elizabeth A. "Atlanta's Pioneer Skyscrapers." *Georgia Review* (Summer, 1965).

_____ "Business Buildings in Atlanta: 1865-1930: A Study in Urban Growth and Form." Ph. D. dissertation, Emory University, 1971.

_____ "Skyscrapers in Atlanta: 1890-1915." M. A. thesis, Emory University, 1962.

King, Maria. "Two Atlanta Churches: An Analysis of Nineteenth Century Revival Architecture." Honors thesis, Emory University, 1975.

King, Spencer Bidwell, Jr. "A Yankee Who Served the South." *Atlanta Historical Bulletin,* XIV (June, 1969).

Morgan, Thomas Henry. "Reminiscences of the Architecture and Architects of Atlanta." *Atlanta Historical Bulletin,* II (June, 1937).

_____ . "The Georgia Chapter of the American Institute of Architects." *Atlanta Historical Bulletin,* VII (September, 1943).

Smith, Francis. "Some Early Architects of Atlanta." Symposium paper, 1966.

White, Dana F., ed. "Frederick Law Olmsted: A Southern Exposure." Papers presented to the Southeastern American Studies Conference, 1973.

Some Sources for Research

Illustrated Books

Art Work in Atlanta. Atlanta, 1895, 1903.

Atlanta Homes 1895-1900. Atlanta, 1895.

The Atlanta Exposition and South Illustrated. Chicago, 1895.

The Gate City: Atlanta Historical, Descriptive and Picturesque. Wisconsin, 1890.

Downing, Walter T. *Domestic Architecture.* Atlanta, 1897.

Atlanta City Directories

Maps and Atlases

Hopkins, G. M. *Atlanta, Georgia.* Baltimore, 1878.

Sanborn Map Company. *Atlanta, Georgia.* New York, 1886, 1892, 1899, 1911.

Building Inspectors Office, City of Atlanta. Building Permits, 1895—.

NOW YOU CAN CLAIM YOUR PIECE OF HISTORY.

You've seen it, read about it, waited for it. One Georgia Center, one of Atlanta's finest structures built in the last two decades, is now ready for immediate occupancy.

Located at the center of it all, One Georgia Center is within walking distance of some of Atlanta's finest restaurants, entertainment facilities, shops and more. If business takes you farther, One Georgia Center offers exceptional access to MARTA's rapid rail system, I-75/I-85 and fast moving surface streets. Airport shuttle and taxi service are readily available.

Inside, discover a new, historically decorated lobby. Offices custom designed to your precise specifications. State-of-the-art comfort and life safety systems. Tenants will enjoy on-site dining and bank facilities. A post office. Fully equipped health club/Wellness Center and hotel. Even 1,000 spaces of covered parking.

The finishing touches are complete on One Georgia Center. Now it's your move.

ONE GEORGIA CENTER

600 West Peachtree Street, N.W.
Atlanta, GA 30308   (404) 872-9200

A Development by Steinemann & Company

19 ROSWELL

Lyon, Elizabeth Anne Mack.
    Atlanta architecture : the Victorian
heritage, 1837-1918, a new edition of
the 1976 catalog / by Elizabeth A.
Lyon. -- [2nd ed.]. -- [Atlanta?] :
Atlanta Historical Society, c1986.
    112 p. : ill. ; 29 cm.
    "A new edition of the 1976 catalog
... prepared for an exhibit at the
Atlanta Historical Society."
    Bibliography: p. 109-110.
    Includes index.